JUST SAY "YES" to LIFE!

Vol. 1

STORIES OF THRIVING AFTER STROKE

Published by

Stroke Awareness Oregon

Bend, Oregon

Advance Praise for *Just Say "Yes" to Life!*

"While suffering a stroke is a devastating, life-altering event, that many patients initially imagine to be worse than dying, *Just Say "Yes" to Life!* is an uplifting book that teaches important lessons. The stories and poems written about and by these stroke survivors are an inspiration to all of us, that confronting physical, cognitive and emotional disability after a stroke with a positive attitude and hard work can result in surprisingly remarkable outcomes and achievements. I would recommend this as required reading for all stroke patients who wish to regain meaning and happiness in their lives." —**Gary K. Steinberg, M.D., Ph.D., Bernard and Ronni Lacroute-William Randolph Hearst Professor of Neurosurgery and the Neurosciences, Founder and Co-Director, Stanford Stroke Center, Former Chair (1995-2020), Department of Neurosurgery, Stanford University School of Medicine**

"After nine years in the NFL and only thirty-one years old, I had a total hip replacement that would drastically change my life forever. The surgery wasn't the tough part—it was the physical therapy and rehab that affects you mentally and emotionally, as well as physically. Never give up on living no matter what circumstances you're in. *Just Say "Yes" to Life!* talks about perseverance, difficult trials, and other real life stories that will motivate you to continue your life journey. Jesus says He came to give life, and give it abundantly. Take that truth and say "Yes" to Life!" —**Neil Lomax, NFL QB St. Louis/Arizona Cardinals, 1981-90, All-American at Portland State University, 1979-80, coach, husband, father, and grandfather**

"Emotional recovery is an important but often overlooked aspect of stroke recovery." —**Maarten G. Lansberg, M.D., Ph.D., Director, Stanford University Stroke Research Fellowship, Professor of Neurology and Neurological Sciences**

"Suffering a stroke can take not only a physical toll on survivors, but an emotional one as well. Stroke survivors can feel isolated, lonely, and misunderstood. *Just Say "Yes" to Life!* is a valuable and much needed resource which provides an uplifting message of recovery and perseverance after stroke. *Just Say "Yes" to Life!* is also important reading for medical professionals as an eloquent and meaningful reminder of the stroke recovery journey. I strongly recommend this book to patients and colleagues alike." —**Kara Flavin, M.D., Physical Medicine and Rehabilitation**

In a day and age when we find ourselves fearing and fighting over relatively petty things, *Just Say "Yes" to Life!* is a reminder of what real fear and true courage is about. These stories of stroke survivors who overcame and are overcoming serious challenges are poignant, hopeful, and deeply personal. Those in this book show us the power of passion and purpose. They give us insight into what we should really be focused on: helping resilient others who want to help themselves—especially in the face of real adversity—in order to build a better life and better communities." —**Ken Streater, international bestselling author of Be the Good and *The Gift of Courage***

"As health care professionals, we at St. Charles Health System understand that having a stroke can be a life-changing event. We also see incredible real-life stories of how our patients thrive in their lives after a stroke every single day. *Just Say "Yes" to Life!* beautifully illustrates the importance of stroke rehabilitation and support to ensure patients regain as much function as possible and continue to thrive." —**Dave Haglund, M.S., P.T., director of St. Charles Health System's Rehabilitation Services**

"Sustaining a life-altering injury or illness leads to many questions and unknowns, and often one of the most challenging aspects is finding resources and community for support. Stroke Awareness Oregon provides critical support to individuals to learn, connect, and ultimately thrive in life after surviving a stroke. At Oregon Adaptive Sports, we rely on organizations like SAO and resources such as *Just Say "Yes" to Life!* to empower athletes to reach out, to break down barriers, and to connect each other to the people and places we all love to be." —**Pat Addabbo, Executive Director, Oregon Adaptive Sports**

"In life, we tend to strive for an effortlessly perfect, memorable journey. However, it is important to understand that encountering setbacks of any magnitude is a part of life. Figuring out how to effectively navigate these hinderances and progress toward positive options that will inspire growth and manageable successes is key. No matter the circumstance, we need to look deep into our souls and make that choice to keep pushing forward. These strides are what create our character, our legacy, and the way we wish to be perceived. *Just Say "Yes" to Life!* is a book that will show you valiant dedication and a sense of pure will that is going to inspire you to conquer life no matter the shape or size of hurdles that may appear before you." —**Marcus Chambers, University of Oregon Track and Field, Seven Time All-American, NCAA Champion, Four-Time Pac-12 Champion, Team USA Track and Field Participant, Motivational Speaker, Co-Founder of the FamFive Youth Scholarship Foundation**

"*Just Say "Yes" to Life!* is filled with stories of triumph. No matter how big or small, it's an acknowledgment to those willing to put in the work. Science teaches us that exercise rewires the brain, and it's obvious through the readings that "going all in" gives us purpose. I highly recommend reading this book." —**Tyler Cuddeford, P.T., Ph.D. Associate Dean, College of Physical Therapy, George Fox University**

This book is dedicated to all stroke warriors, everywhere.

Paperback: ISBN 978-1-7372450-0-1

Edited by Ellen Santasiero ellensantasiero.com
Layout by Lieve Maas brightlightgraphics.com

Library of Congress Control Number: 2021915100

The poem "Healing" by Monza Naff in *Healing the Womanheart*, Wyatt McKenzie Publishing 1999. Reprinted by permission.

Quote by Geoff Babb. Reprinted by permission.
Quotes by Kim O'Kelley-Leigh. Reprinted by permission.
Quote by Marcia Moran. Reprinted by permission.
Quote by Ralph Preston. Reprinted by permission.
Quote by Debra E. Meyerson from *Identity Theft: Rediscovering Ourselves After Stroke*, Andrews McMeel Publishing 2019, p. 205. Reprinted by permission.

Published by Stroke Awareness Oregon
501 C-3, Tax ID 82-4216575

695 SW Mill View Way
Bend, Oregon 97702 USA
strokeawarenessoregon.org

Printed in the United States of America

First Printing, 2021

Disclaimer: This book does not provide medical advice. The information in this book is for educational and inspirational purposes only. Consult a medical professional or health-care provider for advice regarding stroke diagnosis, treatment, and rehab. The views and opinions contained in the stories belong solely to the individual stroke survivors.

"How we move forward after stroke is a choice. Comparing ourselves to our former, successful individuality is only one of many lenses we can look through, and it's probably not the best. Stroke can limit our options, but it does not seal our fate. It is our choice: do we reject our stroke and fight like hell to recover our old life, accept it passively, or embrace the stroke as part of our life and carve a new path with that reality as part of our landscape."

—Debra E. Meyerson

TABLE OF CONTENTS

Foreword by Mike Studer, PT, DPT   xi

Introduction   xiii

The Stories

Asa Pollard   19

Marcia Moran   25

Angel Garcia   35

Beverly Hall   41

Alesha Goodman   49

Joyce Hoffman   59

Keith Taylor   65

Tom Baniewicz   75

Angie Kirk   81

Jim Patterson   87

Roz Dapar   101

Diane M. Barnes   109

Deborah McMahon   119

Ralph Preston   125

Kim O'Kelley-Leigh   137

Debra E. Meyerson   143

Ron Lusk   155

Steve Boatwright   163

Alan Wick   171

Lawnae Hunter   181

Michael Erwin   193
Orlena Shek   201
Gunner Mench   207
Steve Van Houten   215
Geoff Babb   225
Monza Naff   233

Afterword   241
Stroke Awareness Oregon   242
F.A.S.T.   244
Acknowledgements   245
About the Editor   246
Writer Biographies   248
Resources   250
Let's Talk About Stroke!   256

FOREWORD

The human brain is plastic and malleable to the extent that, when certain conditions are met, recovery can continue for more than five years after a stroke. These conditions are quite clear and the science around them is becoming more well-defined every year. Included in the recovery criteria are the motivation to recover, the support to do so safely, medical stability supporting higher intensity exercise, and a proficient rehabilitative team that can both design the interventions and measure the results.

Early in the study of neuroscience, we felt that recovery could not continue after the first three months. This was later advanced to six months and later to one year. We now know, however, that with more precise imaging and more personalized rehabilitation, the brain continues to respond in a "demand and supply" manner. If your brain sees a reachable goal (demand), it will do everything possible to reorganize (supply) the changes needed to accomplish this through neuroplasticity.

The stories in *Just Say "Yes" to Life!* portray excellent examples of the ability to adapt and improve. If you or someone you love has endured a stroke, this book is a must read. These heartfelt and compelling personal stories provide another perspective on life, recovery, and hope for the future. Learning about the recovery of other stroke survivors and their families can and will provide you with the "this is possible" aspect of the "demand and supply" model.

—Mike Studer, PT, DPT

Mike Studer, PT, DPT, MHS, NCS, CEEAA, CWT, CSST, practices in Oregon. He has been a physical therapist since 1991, was board certified in neurologic PT in 1995, and was recognized as Clinician of the Year in the Neurologic and Geriatric Academies of the American Physical Therapy Association (APTA). He received a Fellowship from APTA in 2020. Mike's other honors include the Mercedes Weiss award for service to the Oregon chapter of APTA, and the Clinical Excellence award from both the Academy of Neurologic PT in 2011, and the Academy of Geriatric PT in 2014. He holds a trademark and patent pending in dual task rehabilitation. Over his career, Mike has authored over 30 journal articles, six book chapters, and presents internationally on aging, stroke, motor learning, motivation in rehabilitation, cognition, balance, dizziness, and Parkinson's Disease.

INTRODUCTION

This book grew out of love.

In 2016, I joined a gathering of caring people profoundly affected by the fear, grief, and uncertainty brought on by stroke.

Because my entire career has been dedicated to service endeavors that make others' lives better, I was asked to join the group and guide them in the creation of a new organization, Stroke Awareness Oregon (SAO).

We were meeting in the Bend Fire and Rescue building in Oregon, which sits between the Cascades Mountains to the west, and the high desert to the east. As I looked around the room, I saw doctors, EMTs, a firefighter, and my beloved friend, Lawnae Hunter, who had survived a stroke two years before.

That day I learned about the lack of awareness about the signs of stroke, and the dearth of coordinated support services for those who often require years of rehab and therapies designed specifically for them. I learned that stroke is not "sexy" like heart attack—instead, there is a lot of shame associated with stroke. It shouldn't be that way.

This new organization would seek to dispel the stigma around stroke. It would be dedicated to the early detection of stroke and to survivors. And because survivors long to hear inspiring stories about stroke victims who not only survived, but *thrived* after stroke, a book of inspiring stories would be one of its future offerings.

One of the group's advisors was Dr. Steven Goins, a neurologist in Bend who was passionate about stroke awareness education. He said that if every person in the community could recognize the signs of stroke, victims would get intervention and treatment much more quickly, thus reducing the devastating effects of stroke. This new nonprofit would be the perfect vehicle for what he deemed the most important factor in stroke recovery.

By the end of the meeting, I was hooked.

I was moved by the love expressed that day for stroke-affected people and their families, and I wanted in. Over time I got to know more about the founding board members' passion and commitment to stroke awareness education, and I also got to know survivors, and how stroke robbed them of almost everything. Later, when I was asked to be executive director of the organization, I couldn't say no.

In 2017, founding board members Dr. Dennis Schaberg, Marc Beebe, Mindy Laidlaw, Tom Olsen, Dr. Jim Stone, Lawnae Hunter, Katie Tank, and myself celebrated when SAO received its nonprofit status. Since then, along with other key volunteers and staff, we have grown the organization into what it is today—"a community based nonprofit serving the Central Oregon area ... to increase awareness about stroke symptoms, and prevention, to make F.A.S.T. a household word, and to increase understanding about how stroke survivors and caregivers can receive support for a full, post-stroke life." Today, Dr. Goins recognizes SAO as a crucial partner in state-of-the-art stroke care delivery in Central Oregon.

Three years later, SAO began to breathe life into the idea of the book you are now holding in your hands.

By then the organization had a burgeoning network of personal and professional contacts. SAO board members knew stroke survivors from all over the country, listened deeply to their stories, and befriended many of them. They knew there were myriad stories of people who had not only survived stroke, but were now *thriving*. Yes, their lives are different post-stroke, but they are not diminished in the ways that matter most. Many have achieved and experienced more in life than ever before, and are contributing to their communities in new, different, and more meaningful ways. Moreover, the board knew there were enough stories to collect into a book-length volume.

In early 2020, tapping their network once again, the board found an editor and a group of volunteer writers. Their work fills these pages. The stories in this collection are about people of all ages from all over the U.S. They are mothers and fathers, sons and daughters and spouses. Professionally, they represent a range of vocations including medicine, forestry, and business, the literary and performing arts, and the real estate and food industries.

We hope this collection of stories reaches all those who need it. We hope it is a worthy addition to other fine resources for stroke victims available today.

But most of all, we hope you find these stories hopeful, inspiring, and helpful.

We know the road after stroke is tough, one of the toughest a person may ever face. But we also know it can be traveled and made easier with champions and companions. This book is one of those companions, where every page encourages stroke survivors to just say "Yes" to life!

—Carol Stiles, Executive Director, Stroke Awareness Oregon

THE
STORIES

STORMIN' RECOVERY

Asa Pollard

by Tom Olsen

"Don't let the stroke define who you are.
You are still in charge of your life even though it may
look different than it did before."

In 2016, everything was going Asa Pollard's way.

Asa had always followed his own instincts about how to live life,
and as a young man this practice led him from Austin, TX, where
he was raised, to Paris where he earned a degree from the finest culinary school in the world, Le Cordon Bleu. "I didn't care if I ever
turned it into a career," Asa said. "It was a really expensive gift I gave
myself, and I'm really happy I did it." He delighted in the sublime

satisfaction of setting and achieving one of his own extraordinary goals in life.

Always drawn to the trees, trails, and mountain slopes of the Pacific Northwest, Asa's muse eventually led him to Bend, OR, where he could indulge his passion for snow sports, hiking and rock climbing, and share his culinary skills at The Loft, perhaps the town's most exclusive private dining club. After settling into his new life with a close-knit circle of like-minded friends, he continued his education at Central Oregon Community College (COCC) in the art and science of human movement: kinesiology.

But on New Year's Eve in 2016, Asa woke in the middle of the night to discover his right arm was numb. Thinking nothing of it, he rolled over and fell back asleep. He didn't know yet that a small artery in his brain had burst leaking vital fluid into the surrounding tissue and cutting off the flow of blood and oxygen to a large cluster of essential neurons downstream. In the morning when he got up to go the bathroom, like he'd done hundreds of times before, he collapsed.

"That's really weird," he thought, telling himself, "just get up, get up ... all right, GET UP!" but nothing happened. It was at that instant he realized something had gone terribly wrong, but he didn't know what it was. He'd had a hemorrhagic stroke that killed tissue on the left side of his brain, paralyzing the right side of his body. He dragged himself over to his phone and called his best friend who immediately called an ambulance.

EMTs diagnosed his stroke and flew with Asa, sirens wailing and lights flashing, to the emergency room at St. Charles Medical Center, Central Oregon's most sophisticated trauma center. Diagnostic work-ups confirmed his condition and initial treatment stabilized him. His care was transferred to a hospitalist and consulting neurologist, but Asa was unaware of any of it.

Hours later, Asa woke up alone in his hospital room and slowly realized that one side of his body was paralyzed.

***

The first of Asa's many physical therapists began working on him later that day. With the confidence of the accomplished athlete he was, Asa was eager to get on with his rehab, to overcome his temporary physical challenges, and move on to complete recovery.

"She was a small, older woman, and, man, she kicked my butt," Asa recalled. She made him to get into his wheelchair on his own and rather than push him around from place to place, she made him use his right arm to move around. She flat out refused to help him do what she knew he could—and eventually must—do for himself.

Her approach worked. Asa began to take satisfaction in immediate little victories like wiggling the toes on his right foot: "There we go. Good!" Asa thought. He told himself he'd be back to "normal" in a year.

Within the week he was transferred to transitional care and spent the next three weeks receiving physical, occupational, and speech therapy several times a day. "I loved my physical therapy because I love exercise," Asa said. He hated speech therapy, though. "I wanted to talk so bad and I just couldn't. You're sitting down, and someone's walking around with more coffee, and you want some, and you try to say something, but the words don't come, and you try to raise your hand, but you just can't."

Asa was discharged to the home of a friend who helped him with his Activities of Daily Living (ADLs)—bathing, grooming, dressing, making and eating meals, going to the bathroom, transferring from a one place to another, and walking—and made sure he attended his many outpatient therapy sessions.

About five months into his recovery, Asa realized his early thoughts about a brief recovery were foolish, that his rehab was going to take a long, long time, and he might never get back to "normal." With the slow but awful understanding that he would probably be in some form of rehab for years and likely have some permanent physical disabilities, and after he and his girlfriend decided to split, he hit the bottom of his personal pit of despair.

***

Asa credits Jenny Cruikshank, a close friend and fellow athlete, with bringing him out of his depression and rekindling the inspiration he desperately needed to restore his spirits and kickstart his motivation. She just wouldn't let him lie in idle self-pity for long.

"There's a thing they do every year at COCC called 'storm the stairs'," Asa said. It's a competition of running up and down stairs in one of the college buildings for five kilometers. Jenny got Asa signed up for the event.

"I couldn't run, but [Jenny's] like, 'It's OK. Don't worry. You can do it if you just keep going," he remembered. "Well, she must have told everybody what I was doing, because everybody I saw was cheering me on: 'Go! You got this! You can do this! Yeah!'"

And together, they did it. That was only six months after Asa's stroke.

Completing the event as a new stroke survivor was the most exhilarating moment of his entire recovery, Asa remembered. And while he knew that his life after stroke would never be the same, he also knew his life ahead of him would be immeasurably better than he thought it would be only a few days before.

One day, about the same time Asa successfully stormed the stairs, he carefully navigated his way to his mailbox worried that he might fall. When he did fall—and hard—it actually came as a relief. "I fell. I got up. I was OK. I didn't have to worry about falling like that again."

Small successes led to more small successes, and with the help of a local nonprofit, Asa found himself back on the ski slopes of his beloved Mt. Bachelor.

"The people at Oregon Adaptive Sports learned I was an avid snowboarder before my disability and they really encouraged me to use one of their special snowboards," Asa said. The board took some getting used to, but Asa soon began shredding snow again with as much confidence and fun as ever. Over time, Asa reclaimed many of the sports he enjoyed before his stroke, including running, hiking, and rock climbing.

Today, five years after his stroke, Asa possesses almost all of his physical and verbal abilities, and to watch him walk or hear him talk, you would never guess he's a stroke survivor. But he knows all too well what he's been through, and is exquisitely aware of the stroke's lingering effects. "When I get really tired, I have pauses that I never had before and it's really obvious to me, even if it's not obvious to other people," he said.

Asa earned his bachelor's in kinesiology from Oregon State University-Cascades, and he's finishing a master's in education from George Fox College. His goal is to become a licensed Oregon educator. But by far the greatest event in Asa's life was falling in love with Johanna, a registered nurse. They were married in Bend this past May. "Life is great," Asa said.

***

Asa's advice for new stroke survivors? "Don't let the stroke define who you are. You are still in charge of your life even though it may look different than it did before." He also stresses the importance of celebrating the small gains made during physical, occupational, or speech therapy. For male stroke survivors, Asa has advice about something he wishes was more frequently discussed in men's support groups. "It's natural for men to wonder whether their sex life [and that of their partner] will change as a result of their disability. I know I did," Asa said. "But I learned that while a stroke may mean making some changes for both of you, it is rarely the end of a full and satisfying sex life."

Asa's close friends were his essential support early on, but he was his own closest caregiver for most of his recovery. Still, he does have some encouragement for family caregivers and loved ones. "Both of your lives have changed, and you may not like it, but be patient and don't give up! Your life will get better! Keep striving, because it's going to get better."

AHEAD OF THE CURVE

Marcia Moran

by Lili Alpaugh

"Never. Give. Up. *Ever*. … And keep looking for
new treatments!"

It was a Sunday morning in March 2014 when Marcia Moran woke
up in her home in Centreville, VA, looking forward to meeting
her friend Rochele for breakfast. The sun was streaming through
the windows, something she loved to see. Jim, her husband, had
already gotten up. Marcia sat up and noticed she felt a little odd.
She realized she wouldn't be able to have breakfast with Rochele and
texted her. Before hitting "send," she noticed she couldn't read what
she'd written. While that normally would've been cause for alarm,
Marcia thought, *oh well, I guess I'm just tired.* She laid down, turned

over and soon developed a severe headache. Somehow she fell back asleep in spite of the pain.

When she woke the second time, she immediately knew something was wrong. She couldn't move the right side of her body. She needed Jim's help, but he was downstairs with the TV blaring, and the bedroom door was closed.

With great effort, Marcia hoisted and rolled herself off the bed onto the floor, and dragged herself towards the door using her left hand, digging her fingers into the pile carpet. Her head was pounding. Once she reached the door, she reached up several times before she opened it. She was so sweaty and tired, she rested there for a while to take a break.

She eventually made it into the hallway and inched herself towards the staircase. Her strength soon gave out completely and she couldn't move at all. Suddenly, something fell and crashed to the floor. Jim heard it and came up the stairs. "Marcia! Are you all right?!" he called. Marcia couldn't answer; she realized she couldn't speak. Jim immediately called 911 and paramedics rushed her to the ER.

Marcia was fifty-three at the time, a slender, fit woman who ran three or four times a week and worked at her own business as a marketing consultant. Besides running, she kayaked and hiked with Jim and enjoyed time at their lake house. She also painted and practiced meditation. As far as she knew, she was very healthy. Then the stroke occurred. What happened?

Marcia's stroke resulted from an internal carotid artery dissection, which caused clots to form and travel to her brain, causing an ischemic stroke. Carotid artery dissection is a rare event, responsible for only one to two percent of all strokes. The doctors couldn't explain why her artery tore, but a congenital weakness in the artery may have been a possibility.

Physical therapy began on her first day in the hospital, while she was still in the ER. The PT evaluated Marcia, put a belt around her waist, and with some assistance from the PT, Marcia stood up to walk. Her right leg was extremely weak. "I lurched forward, hiking my right leg up to clear it, with my foot turning outward. I felt like Frankenstein in Gene Wilder's movie, *Young Frankenstein*! But I made it all the way around the nurses' station and back to bed. I was ecstatic!"

Marcia was moved to acute care for four days and then spent two weeks in inpatient rehab. For her, occupational therapy was the hardest thing. She had to learn how to tie her shoes, take a shower, clip and unclip things, and other basic self-care skills. She was surprised to find out how difficult even brushing her teeth was. "I started brushing with my right hand, but it had a mind of its own. I switched to my left hand, but that proved to be messy, too. When I rinsed, I kept spitting on my hand, not in the sink. It took me quite a while to learn that spitting in the sink and arm movement have to be coordinated."

Marcia was quickly finding out that stroke survivors have to relearn the most basic tasks in a step-by-step fashion; many muscles have to work together in a timed, coordinated way to accomplish a simple movement, something most people take for granted.

The stroke affected Marcia's speech the most. In the case of language, the brain has to do a whole lot of things before a word can leave one's lips. She had both an apraxia of language and aphasia, which meant her muscles not only had trouble forming words and sounds, but she also struggled to find the word in her mind to begin with. At times, she struggled to understand the meaning of words she'd known all her life, and had to relearn how to write and spell many words.

She was able to read but often had trouble remembering what she'd read. She could understand questions being asked of her, and knew what she wanted to say, but responding through speaking or writing was a whole other ball game. Determined to speak normally again, she worked especially hard in speech therapy, and actually enjoyed it.

Swallowing was also an issue at first. She'd been placed on a restricted diet of pureed food and thickened liquids. One day, she was given a regular tray of food for lunch by accident. She didn't think anything of it. She began eating; it was not long before she choked. The nursing staff came and saw what had happened, and they admonished Marcia for eating that food. "That hurt emotionally," said Marcia. "My higher thinking skills had left the building. It didn't occur to me that I wasn't ready for a regular diet." Fortunately, Marcia did not aspirate the food or have other problems as a result.

When Marcia returned home, she continued all three therapies with home-health therapists for six weeks, and eventually went to outpatient therapy for another six. After that, she didn't want her progress to end, so she hired her own physical therapist for a year to work with her on more advanced mobility skills. She worked out every single day, including performing some cross-body movements to engage both sides of her brain, and never skipped a workout, even though sometimes she was tempted to do so. Over the next year, her mobility skills returned for the most part, but she still had pain in her entire right side and cramping in her right foot.

Marcia's goals were to return one hundred percent to what she was doing before: working as a marketeer, running, and training for 5K races. She even started running outdoors, but noticed that her right foot moved more slowly than before. Undaunted, she kept at it, but she fell and dislocated her right elbow. She then realized 5K races would be out of the question.

After the first year, Marcia's aphasia had improved somewhat, but was not always as fluid or spontaneous as she would've liked. She came to accept that due to the complex language and speaking demands of being a marketeer, she'd never return to operating her own business. But it was important that she didn't give up on herself. She decided to find work elsewhere. She updated her resume, including that she'd had a stroke, and applied for five positions.

She landed two phone interviews, which initially was very encouraging. She prepared and felt confident about how she would answer interview questions. But in both interviews, Marcia became mute when asked certain things. The interviewers tried to be patient and let Marcia take her time, but the higher-level demands of speaking about job skills proved to be too challenging. She didn't get either position.

She realized she needed additional practice at speaking. She sought out career-transition coaching and she joined Toastmasters, where she could practice conversing with other people on various topics other than the everyday conversations she had at home. She also participated in stroke support groups to further improve her speaking skills. These practices were certainly helpful, but she still wasn't where she wanted and needed to be.

As for her pain, Marcia still had unrelenting severe pain in her right shoulder, hip, and knee from the stroke. Wanting to enhance the traditional treatments with holistic treatments, she went to an acupuncturist for help with pain relief. This acupuncturist performed traditional acupuncture on Marcia, but also did a comprehensive food sensitivity panel, and discovered that she was sensitive to a lot of things in her diet (dairy, eggs, gluten, soy, yeast, etc.) Marcia altered her diet, adding in some recommended supplements, and also underwent Pulsed Electromagnetic Field Therapy with this acupuncturist. All of this was intended to decrease inflammation in her body, and it worked to a large degree; her pain decreased and she could move a little more easily.

Marcia continued to search for novel treatments that might help her aphasia. She was still having trouble getting her thoughts out when conversations went deep and was frustrated with having to use sub-stitute words at times for the words she really wanted. As the founder and owner of a successful business, Marcia was used to taking charge and innovating when necessary. She kept researching and asked for advice from friends and other stroke survivors, and what they told her changed her life.

***

Marcia was introduced to two additional interventions for stroke. The first was Low-Level Laser Light Therapy (Erchonia Corporation's 635 nm), which she tried two years post-stroke. "Laser therapy helped," she said, "but it didn't take me all the way. It was like I had two people talking in my head. The words I wanted to say, and the words I could say—sometimes."

A year and a half following that, she tried Micro Current Neurofeed-back (MCN by IASIS Technologies). This treatment made the biggest difference. MCN helps the brain reorganize and reboot, to normalize brainwaves. After sixteen sessions, Marcia improved *dramatically* in both the physical and speech areas. MCN proved to be almost a magic bullet for her aphasia; now, it's almost completely gone.

Marcia feels strongly that there is a need to start using these forms of Low-Level Laser and MCN alongside the traditional rehab therapies. At a minimum, she'd like to see rehab professionals inform patients about these treatments when they leave rehab. She emphasizes that people will get different results; some get more benefit than others, but they won't know unless they try. In Marcia's case, she said, "If I'd had these earlier on in my recovery, perhaps I would've made even more gains, and recovered a lot faster."

During her recovery, Marcia wrote a book about her stroke, *Stroke Forward*. In it, she recounts her own journey, and that of her husband, along with the various treatments that helped her, information and research about those treatments, and other resources. The book is written for both survivors and their caregivers.

***

Vital to Marcia's recovery was the support of her husband Jim. "Jim has been an amazing caregiver and advocate," Marcia said. "He arranged for all of my early therapy and made sure I got there. He's had to be my voice in so many situations, and being a quiet guy, it's brought him out quite a bit! The stroke changed his life just as much as it changed mine."

The couple had planned to travel to Ireland to renew their wedding vows in 2014, but the stroke called that off. In 2018, they were able to make the trip. "The whole thing was magical," recalled Marcia. "We stayed at the Abbeyglen Castle Hotel, and our ceremony was held out on the patio next to a beautiful, running fountain. It was a bright, sunny day, but a bit windy. My multicolored dress looked like someone had painted watercolor splotches on it as it blew about! This ceremony meant so much to me. Jim and I have always been close, but sharing the experience of the stroke has brought us even closer."

A highlight of the trip occurred at the Cliffs of Moher on the Atlantic coast. One afternoon, after the coastal fog receded back out to sea, they hiked up the highest peak of the cliffs and then over to O'Brien's Tower, built in 1835 as an observation tower. The waves crashed below along the rocky shore, and the trail was steep. "It was scary navigating the steep parts, but with a little help from Jim, I made it! I felt really proud of myself that day."

Today, Marcia says she is 95 percent back to normal. When the pandemic is over, she plans to continue her advocacy work for stroke survivors by teaching others, spreading the word about novel treatments, and doing some motivational speaking. She also plans to return to some other form of work.

"My recovery has been helped by my entrepreneurial spirit, I think. My motto is: Never. Give. Up. *Ever.* You don't know how well you can become. Do your exercises *every single day,* and continue for years if necessary. And keep looking for new treatments!

Passion

Passion is the pulse
of the willow's breath you watch
beyond the green paint
of hospital walls, the force
in the hurricane of lies
you tell yourself
to stay aloft in dead air,
the ferocity in your face
when you take your first steps
after the stroke, the staying power
of brave ink, however shaky,
on white paper
when the idea of "word"
is still beyond all thought.

by Monza Naff ©2007

Angel Garcia, right, with his Uncle Hector

BACK IN BUSINESS
Angel Garcia

by Jake Sheaffer

"Hit rehab as hard you can within the first year.
Statistics show that's when the bulk of your recovery occurs."

In 2016, Angel Garcia, a laid back seventeen-year-old, was attending Mountain View High School in Bend, OR. Back then, he planned to enroll at the University of Oregon (UO) to major in sport business after graduation. At school he ran track and played soccer. Outside of school, he played for the Rush Soccer Club, played pickup basketball, and worked as a dietary aide at Fox Hollow Independent Living.

One summer day between his junior and senior year, at home with his family, Angel felt a numbness in his arm and then blacked out. Weeks later, he woke up in St. Charles Medical Center and learned that he had suffered a stroke and had been in a coma for two weeks.

The damage from his stroke limited many of his motor functions and left him unable to sit up or speak. His doctors only knew that Angel's mind hadn't been affected by the stroke because he used his smartphone to text updates to family and friends.

Those family and friends frequently visited Angel in the hospital. Noah, a good friend since elementary school, recalled Angel's discomfort with people seeing him after the stroke. Angel's sense of humor was still intact, though—he eventually did wheelchair races in the hall with his friends. Angel didn't want anyone to accommodate him, said Noah.

"If someone tried to let him win, he'd ram into them with his wheelchair."

Angel went from an active life to eight hours a day in rehab, surrounded by medical professionals and an elder population. "It was a setting I never thought to find myself in just a few months before," said Angel. From lifting weights for the fall soccer season to learning how to pick up utensils, Angel found himself in a new world that included online schooling, countless medical appointments, and the unenviable task of relearning many skills he could perform without hesitation earlier that summer.

In the first year after his stroke, Angel retreated inward. He went from eight hours a day at physical therapy to eight hours a week, preferring the comfort of his bedroom to the unpleasantness of rehab clinics. Embarrassed to spend a lot of time with friends, and uncomfortable with letting people see how he walked or hear him speak, he credited the blunt advice of a friend as the spark that got him out of his rut.

"You're not dead. Stop feeling sorry for yourself," they would tell him. That "kick in the ass," as he described it, was what he needed to see that he had much to live for, such as his relationships with friends, which remained strong. His friends were supportive, too. They made sure their activities included accessibility for Angel if he needed it.

Over time Angel started to focus on his future again. After returning to high school almost two years after his stroke, he graduated from Mountain View and enrolled at Central Oregon Community College (COCC) with the intention to eventually transfer to the UO. He and his family also found a new primary care doctor committed to understanding what caused Angel's stroke, rather than treating him as an elder stroke survivor, as many previous inpatient staff did.

With help from his family and countless appointments with specialists around the state, Angel discovered the cause of his stroke. It wasn't genetics or bad habits, it was a malformation in his brain. A vein was connected to an artery instead of to another vein, and that caused a burst to occur in his brain. It was one of those one in a million medical moments.

Armed with information and renewed confidence from his friends, Angel's perspective has changed in the years since his stroke. "My outlook is more scholar-focused than before my stroke," he said. "My goal is still to attend the University of Oregon for sport business, and then after that an MBA. I also just want to get back to as normal as possible. That's why I keep a positive outlook. I really can't afford to look at it in any other way." Noah agreed. "Angel works harder now. He gets committed to something and he finishes it."

Rehab is still difficult for Angel. Within four years he's been assigned three different therapists, but now they can focus on the specifics of his stroke. He has learned to empathize with his fellow elder stroke survivors, too, and he's far more aware of the different possibilities that can befall someone similar in age to him.

Meeting new people and fostering friendships has been difficult for Angel since his stroke, as he spent the first couple of years attending school online. Once he started at COCC two years ago he started to meet new people, but in 2020, like most of the country and world, his education and social life was pushed back onto the internet and video screens. Even though he counts himself as a veteran of online learning, he is excited to get back to physical classrooms once it's safe to do so.

Angel reflected on the advice he would offer to medical staff working with stroke survivors.

"Understand who your patient is," he said. "Some survivors you'll have to be more patient with, more careful with. I prefer a rough honesty, to take those big leaps, but that style of help isn't for everyone. If you can understand a survivor's motivations, then what follows will be more successful than if you hadn't taken the time to learn about the person at all."

He also has advice for stroke survivors who are early in their recovery. "You should hit rehab as hard you can within the first year. Statistics show that's when the bulk of your recovery occurs."

Noah credits Angel's recovery in part to Angel's competitiveness. He recalled one day before the stroke when they were on a basketball court playing best out of seven for Angel's Kobe basketball shoes. Noah was up 3 to 0, and during the fourth game, Angel landed on Noah's foot and fractured his ankle. Angel went to the hospital and then showed up at phys ed class on crutches. "We were playing pickleball, and he put his crutches down and went full force in class!" laughed Noah. "I'm sure his competitiveness helped him a lot with recovery."

Now, at twenty-one, Angel wears a green UO hoodie with a large yellow "O" in the center of it. He's not quite to the UO yet, but in the final year of an associate's degree from COCC. He is committed to continuing his studies next fall as an Oregon Duck.

After that he plans to take a few years off before pursuing his MBA and a future career in the sport industry, either in marketing or at an agency. His throughline goal though, since before his stroke has remained the same: to make a comfortable life for himself with a stable family and a stable life. An admirable goal for anyone, but a remarkable and wise choice for a seventeen-year-old stroke survivor to pursue and follow through with at twenty-one.

NEVER A QUITTER

Beverly Hall

by Diane Huie Balay

"You will get tired and frustrated and upset,
but your attitude is vital to recovery. Don't focus on
what you can't do—focus on what you are able to do."

On an early morning in May 1999, the Reverend Beverly Hall was
in the middle of making love to her husband, when she suddenly had
her first stroke.

"All I could think of to say was 'I can't breathe,'" she said. "I was very
scared. I didn't know what was happening."

Her husband Jerry, an Air Force reservist, called for an ambulance and got her dressed while they were waiting for it to arrive.

In the hospital, the Rev. Hall, known to almost everyone as Rev. Bev, learned she had a stroke on the right side of her brain. She couldn't talk. She couldn't see out of her left eye. She couldn't walk. Her left side was paralyzed.

"I asked God why. Why me? Why now? I was angry at myself," she said. "I must have done something terrible," she thought, "and the stroke was my fault."

But she did not want to die. "I had too much unfinished business I had to take care of," she said.

At the time of her stroke, she was at the end of her service as pastor of Coalburg United Methodist Church near Hubbard, OH, and she wanted to be able to say goodbye to her congregation. She wanted to see her daughter Amber graduate from high school. And, in September, she wanted to go to England where she had a scholarship to work on her doctorate at Oxford Brookes University.

Rev. Bev was in the hospital for three weeks. The superintendent of her church's district asked her if she would take disability leave. Her answer was a resounding "no!" "I wanted to be useful as long as possible," she said. "I fought really hard to continue to work."

Those fighting words perfectly describe Rev. Bev and her attitude toward life. At then four feet nine inches tall, this Mighty Mouse of a woman has the heart and determination of a lioness. Show her a barrier to her goal and she will go over, around, under or through it until she achieves that goal. Her stroke presented monumental barriers and they wouldn't be her last.

When Rev. Bev came home, Jerry still had to work, so the small community she served helped take care of her. A neighboring couple brought her food and helped her shower. They were delightful, she said. "We had fun." Her father, Robert Burley, became her mainstay by driving her to call on her church members.

Rev. Bev's speech came back but she couldn't remember words easily. She couldn't write, but she could print and type on the computer with one finger. She was still in a wheelchair, but she was determined to stand up during her last sermon at the Coalburg Church.

"I literally had to cling to the lectern," she said, "but I did it! The congregation gave me a standing ovation!" That afternoon, the church's clown ministry gave a performance. The clowns were mostly teenagers of the congregation, but their ages ranged from six-years-old to eighty-one. Her clown name was Butterfly. Before the stroke, "I would just flutter by with big antennae on my headband," she said.

She brought a clown ministry to all of the churches she served thereafter. Most of her clothes reflect her love of butterflies. Even in her formal portrait, a beautiful, sparkling butterfly is pinned on her suit jacket.

After her stroke, although the doctor recommended physical therapy, Rev. Bev was preparing to leave the country. She worked on physical exercises at home using pulleys and bands. She squeezed a rubber ball shaped like a brain to strengthen her right hand.

"Every day was a victory," she said, "like putting on my socks, or cooking something simple like a grilled cheese sandwich."

She already had a plan for physical therapy while she was in England.

With the attack on the World Trade Center still two years in the future, Rev. Bev's father was able to wheel her to the gate when it came time to board the plane for England. She was able to walk with a cane down the aisle to the restroom while on the plane. Throughout the flight and through customs at Heathrow Airport in London, airline personnel were kind and helpful, she said. But on the bus to Oxford, she couldn't understand the accent of the bus driver when he called her stop. She missed it and the bus driver dropped her at a taxi stand, wheelchair and all, in a completely different location.

Jet-lagged and exhausted, she took a taxi to her lodgings in the village of Horton-cum-Studley. She found the key under the mat of the two-story house and crawled up the stairs to her room. Immediately afterward, she went next door to the local church where church members warmly welcomed her and invited her to supper.

The University was about seven miles away from her lodging, and Rev. Bev reached it by a combination of village volunteer drivers, public buses, and walking with 10 pounds of books and papers on her back. And she still couldn't see with her left eye. At the university, she studied Wesleyan theology and researched the women followers of John Wesley, the Church of England priest who, along with his brother Charles, founded the Methodist movement in the eighteenth century. She discovered many cases of domestic and societal abuse among these women.

True to her plan, Rev. Bev got her physical therapy by cleaning nine village houses plus the village hall with all of its bathrooms and showers, and ironing. She walked between properties. But while on a stepladder cleaning a chandelier, she had her second stroke. Somehow, she managed to limp home. The doctor at the National Health Service agreed that she had a stroke, then sent her home with no further treatment, she said.

Rev. Bev returned to the States in May 2001.

"Two years earlier, I arrived in England in a wheelchair," she said, and even though she'd suffered a second stroke, when she returned she "walked off the plane in the United States carrying my suitcase."

September 2001 began a difficult period in Rev. Bev's life, as well as the nation's. On Sept. 11, she was at the hospital when her father had surgery and the world watched the devastating terrorist attacks on the World Trade Center on television. The next day, her father died. "It was hard for me," she said. "As an only child, everything was left up to me."

She and Jerry sorted through everything at her dad's house, and cleaned and prepared the house for its eventual sale. In addition, she had been appointed as pastor to a new church, Marengo United Methodist Church, in Marengo, OH.

Her tenure at Marengo was extremely stressful, she recalled. Her health deteriorated badly while she also finished her doctorate, mostly online, at St. Paul's School of Theology. She had crushing headaches and 28 TIAs (mini-strokes) that made fulfilling her many church responsibilities an enormous struggle. It was difficult to get up and down the steps to the altar area to lead the service and preach. A neurologist finally diagnosed her problems as moyamoya, an extremely rare brain disease. The prognosis was bleak. She was given two years to live.

Some church members were not happy with Rev. Bev. Some accused her of lying about the disease, she said, because they had never heard of it. Others did not want their pastor to die on their watch. Basically, some very vocal members wanted her gone.

"The most frustrating thing," she said, "was that everybody, and I mean everybody, even the church's district leadership, said I needed to quit ministry. I needed to take disability. I said, 'Sorry. I'm not.'" Her husband Jerry was the only one who agreed with her.

As a result, in 2006 Rev. Bev left the Marengo Church for her new assignment as pastor of Chapel Hill United Methodist Church in Belleville, OH. There, the congregation held a healing service for her, loved her, and cared for her for eight years, she said.

In the meantime, Rev. Bev refused to die. She was not about to give up without a fight. She searched the Internet until she found a surgeon who specialized in moyamoya, Dr. Gary Steinberg of the Stanford Moyamoya Center in Palo Alto, CA. When she contacted Dr. Steinberg, he told her, "Get out here right away!"

Because Jerry was deployed to Iraq in April 2007, church member Jackie Bollinger accompanied Rev. Bev to help her through the surgery and recovery. The two women stayed in Palo Alto for four weeks while the doctor performed two successful surgeries.

"The surgery was a miracle," Rev. Bev said. "It stopped the pain. The headaches and the TIAs were gone. And, surprisingly, the sight returned to my left eye. Every day, I get up and say, 'Thank you, Lord.'"

Rev. Bev and Jackie returned to Ohio on Monday of the first week in May. The following weekend, Rev. Bev preached the sermon and performed a wedding.

In July, Rev. Bev developed an infection and returned to California for tests and intravenous antibiotic treatment. While there, she wrote the paper "Appreciative Inquiry and Transformational Learning Design" which she presented the following month in England at the Oxford Institute held at Christ Church College, Oxford. She was one of 200 Wesleyan Scholars invited from around the world.

Throughout the entire ordeal of strokes and stroke recovery, Rev. Bev continued writing and presenting papers at conferences. Some were on domestic violence, some on disabilities. One was titled

"Theology in Harry Potter." Another was "Pineapple Hospitality in a Fruitcake World." And she served as East Ohio Conference Dis-Ability Team Leader from 2010 until 2020.

***

Rev. Bev served two additional churches before she and Jerry retired in July of 2020 to the high green hills of North Carolina, Jerry's home state. Their present hometown, Lenoir, is in the foothills of the Blue Ridge Mountains near the ranch where Jan Karon, one Rev. Bev's favorite authors, grew up. They are also near Blowing Rock, NC, the charming mountain town considered to be the setting for Karon's enormously popular Mitford series.

So, is Rev. Bev finally kicking back, reading her entire collection of Jan Karon's Mitford books, and enjoying some of the most beautiful scenery in the United States? Of course not, at least not entirely! She never gives up. She is on the National Ministers With DisAbilities Committee. She is writing a book on her computer, one finger at a time, writing and teaching Bible study classes on Zoom, and serving wherever she feels needed.

***

The Reverend Doctor Beverly Hall can now walk, although slowly, without a cane. She hears from her daughters Courtney and Amber and her grandson, Amber's son Garth, and visits them on Google's Duo.

She encourages stroke survivors to take it one day, one step at a time. "You are not your disease nor are you defined by any disability. Focus on having a better day each day. Push yourself but remember you will have limits. You will get tired and frustrated and upset, but your attitude is vital to recovery. Don't focus on what you can't do—focus on what you are able to do. Be an inspiration for someone else."

"Living in my abilities brings me energy and keeps me happy. It keeps me out of "poor me" out of 'yeah, look what happened to me." Yeah, look what happened to me, I lost my left side and now I am defying it. They told me I was semi-paralyzed and I said no. Period. I said no, and I began to defy it and I invite you to defy your disability. Go where they say you can't go."

—Kim O'Kelley-Leigh

A DRIVING FORCE

Alesha Goodman

by Jake Sheaffer

"I once threw a canister of my supplement powder at the wall
and dented it. That's something I can't imagine ever
doing before my stroke, but it's just another part
of my recovery to work on."

On an early October weekend in 2019, Alesha Goodman and her longtime boyfriend Drew hiked over 50 miles of rugged desert landscape in the Ochoco National Forest in Central Oregon. They were on a nine-day hunting trip they'd been planning for months. While Drew streaked up the steep slopes of sagebrush and loose rock, Alesha tarried behind breathing heavily, fighting the searing pain radiating from the base of her skull. An active thirty-four-year-old who frequented local gyms, walked her dog daily, and hiked on weekends, Alesha never suspected the severe neck pain and nausea she'd had for the past week and a half were signs of an impending stroke. And not just one stroke, but two. Two potentially fatal strokes that would occur within an hour of each other the day after she returned from the Ochocos.

An only child, Alesha was close to her parents and her grandmother who lived on her parents' property later in life. As a kid, she delivered newspapers in her Bend, OR neighborhood, and in her spare time, she wrote children's books for fun and read voraciously, prompting close friends to refer to her as a "living encyclopedia of odd information."

On the Monday morning after she got home, Alesha sat in traffic at a parkway off-ramp, still in discomfort from the neck pain and the nausea. She had new symptoms, too, dizziness and feeling faint. Regardless of the pain, she readied herself for work, but she had an uneasy feeling about her job.

Over the weekend, Alesha had received multiple text messages from her employer, a jewelry company in Central Oregon, about an issue with her company email and password, but with no cell reception, she couldn't respond to her manager's concerns. After searching through Alesha's desk for her email password and not finding it, but instead finding an important legal document she'd already dealt with but had not yet disclosed to her boss, the company hired a specialist to get around the digital safeguards. That day, Alesha was let go from her position.

"I'm not going to say I wasn't upset about losing my job," Alesha said, "but I wasn't devastated. I felt there was something better out there for me and now I had time to find it. I was still in a tremendous amount of pain as I left."

When Alesha first noticed her symptoms, she and Drew chalked it up to the monthly cervicogenic headaches she'd had for the previous four years. "As Drew would tell it," Alesha said, "when my neck would go out, I would be down for the count the whole weekend." But Alesha recognized that there was something different about the pain that preceded the strokes: there was no accompanying headache. At home that night, she and Drew settled in for a movie. Partway through the film, Alesha's neck started to hurt even more, and she had difficulty holding her head up.

The next day she made an appointment with a chiropractor. The severe neck pain caused symptoms that now felt more akin to a migraine. Her chiropractor attributed the soreness to her neck being out of place, and they worked on her head, neck, and spine under that assumption.

Alesha had been seeing a chiropractor since a traffic accident in 2015 that had left her with a muscle strain and whiplash. "I don't have any proof of it, but I believe that this was the inciting incident to my strokes," Alesha said. The next day brought no relief. Alesha's mother Christi helped her get to an urgent care clinic, but the staff there thought the cause of her sore neck was from muscle strain while working out. They prescribed her pain pills and muscle relaxers.

"Of course, the pain didn't go away, even after taking pills, so I had Drew take me over to the ER at St. Charles," Alesha said. "And kind of like urgent care, even after a CTA, they thought it had something to do with my muscles and advised me to rest."

After returning from the hunting trip and losing her job, Alesha was sitting in her car at a stop sign outside of her former workplace—coincidentally just a couple hundred feet from where her father had died—waiting for traffic to pass.

"That's when I heard my dad," Alesha said. In 2012, her father had died suddenly from cardiac arrest, a loss still difficult for her to talk about. "I could hear him tell me to 'back up now,' and thank goodness I listened."

With the advice from her father echoing in her mind, Alesha backed up and parked near the curb. "I remember taking a sip of water after backing up, and that's when a strong tingling sensation went down the right side of my body from my head to my toes," she recalled.

The interior of Alesha's vertebral arteries, major arteries in the back of the neck similar to the carotid arteries in the front of the neck, had torn apart internally and the first of her two strokes that day immobilized her entire right side. She knew she was having a stroke.

Because she was so close to her former workplace, Alesha grabbed her phone and told Siri to call her former boss. Her boss didn't pick up, so she called another employee. "She picked up. Part of my mouth was drooping at this point, so I told her through slurred speech to call 911."

After she hung up, she felt compelled to talk with her father. "I remember in that moment of fear I asked him if he could maybe talk to God and see if he could help me out with this because I really wanted to keep going with this life," Alesha recounted.

Unable to call Drew herself, a woman from the office got through to him at the Subaru dealership where he worked. Alesha waited for longer than she expected for the paramedics and fire department to arrive. She later learned that an emergency dispatcher misrouted the medical personnel and didn't take the call from Alesha's co-worker as seriously as they should have.

By the time the ambulance arrived, her boss and most of her former co-workers were either outside with Alesha or watching from the windows of the office. The paramedics started an early assessment of a panic attack.

"They put electrodes from my chest down my stomach and on my legs then asked me if I could stand up, but when I tried to answer them, all I could do was slur answers while keeping my eyes shut. My right eye was fixed in one position, and it was just easier to close them both," Alesha explained.

With her one good hand, Alesha grabbed the door frame of her car, pulled herself up and then leaned against the vehicle. Again, through slurred speech, Alesha tried to explain to the medics about her obvious stroke symptoms, as did her former co-workers, but they didn't listen. Since she was able to stand up and she was otherwise a healthy woman in her mid-thirties, they assumed she was having a panic attack or was just dehydrated. They convinced her not to take an ambulance to the hospital as they worried about what it might cost her financially.

"When Drew got there, the paramedics dragged my slouching body over to Drew's truck. The two of us headed over to the hospital," Alesha said.

On the way, the droop in Alesha's face went away and her speech returned to almost normal, but just before they got to the emergency room drop-off area at St. Charles, the second stroke hit. Drew lifted her out of the truck and into a wheelchair, but because he couldn't remain parked in that area, Alesha was left to talk to the receptionist in the ER while he moved his truck. "I felt like they were treating me like I had a broken toe because there was no urgency on anyone's part other than Drew's. They asked me my date of birth, and I slurred the answer. I was just in complete disbelief and in a fog because I was going through a second stroke, and the medical staff went about it with no hurry."

By the time Drew parked his truck and made his way into the hospital, Alesha's mother had arrived and doctors had Alesha hooked up to machines and were checking her vitals. "As he tells it, I had almost a split personality when they were poking, prodding, and hooking me up to the different machines," Alesha said.

A CT scan revealed that both of Alesha's vertebral arteries had dissected, causing "bilateral vertebral artery dissection," a condition that her doctor explained was like the interior layers of a garden hose tearing apart leading to blood clotting between the layers and ultimately, the clots were blocking blood flow up to her brain. She was immediately put on an intravenous blood thinner to prevent the possibility of a stroke, or so they thought.

During her ER visit two weeks prior, nothing on the scans showed what the medical staff was seeing now. Now they knew her neck pain was due to the arteries in her neck tearing apart. "I thought that this had to be a one in a hundred thousand chance of happening, but later on, when I brought this up to the doctors, they told me I was the third woman in Bend to have this happen in the past year or two. Each one of us in our thirties and each of us with a prior history of whiplash."

After the scan, she was sent to the intensive care unit where she remembered a large TV screen or monitor with her vitals on it. She was then taken down for an MRI and told that she had suffered two strokes in her cerebellum from the vertebral artery dissections.

For the rest of the evening, every hour, ICU nurses would check Alesha's blood. If things got worse, she would be flown over the mountains to Oregon Health & Science University because St. Charles was not set up to deal with a case like hers.

Some time that evening, her mother and Drew left. "There were IVs in both of my arms, I couldn't get out of bed, and I wasn't allowed to eat anything solid. I was allowed a milkshake, which I was excited about because I hadn't eaten anything all day and now was dehydrated. I was also allowed some ice chips, but that was it," Alesha said.

While drinking the milkshake and watching *The Simpsons,* Alesha felt a tingling sensation down the right side of her body and then her limbs started to feel numb. Alesha worried it was another stroke coming on and immediately buzzed for the nurse. The lines of the cartoon on the television started to disappear. "I wouldn't say my life flashed before my eyes, but I started to think about my mom and Drew, and I started to talk to my dad again. Asking him again to not let this be the end. Of course, if it was another stroke, there wasn't much the hospital could have done at that point."

After her scare with the milkshake and *The Simpsons* disappearing from the screen, staff informed her that she was experiencing the "waxing and waning" of a stroke due to low blood flow. On the following day, the hospital moved her out of the ICU and to the orthopedic and neurology floor because her mind and body were already improving.

She remained in the hospital for the next five and a half days, but she was moved off of intensive occupational or physical therapy because she could walk with a walker and because she could swallow normal food. After her discharge, St. Charles referred her to a neurologist, but she had to seek out rehab on her own. The physical therapy she received was primarily through a private clinic, Rebound Physical Therapy. And then, when someone donated a Feldenkrais Neuromuscular Therapy package to Stroke Awareness Oregon, Alesha was chosen as the recipient.

But for Alesha, the physical recovery was not her only concern. Finding help with mental health was at the top of her priority list.

She had found counseling helpful when she went away to college because the loss of her family structure was challenging for her. The day after her stroke, Alesha immediately looked for mental health resources. "I feel like most everyone could use a better support system when dealing with something so important," Alesha said.

The after effects of a stroke, or "aftershocks," as Drew characterizes them, vary in each survivor, and for Alesha, one of them is a change in her temperament. "Unfortunately—and fortunately—it's just Drew and my mother who have seen my anger," Alesha said. "It's not like anything they do intentionally, but one minute I'm fine, and the next minute the anger is just there, and I know it's because of the stroke. I once threw a canister of my supplement powder at the wall and dented it. That's something I can't imagine ever doing before my stroke, but it's just another part of my recovery to work on."

***

Along with the extensive forms of physical, mental, and emotional therapy, Alesha said she owes so much of her survival and optimism to the strong bond she developed with her parents as an only child and her zeal for knowledge.

Before she had her strokes, Alesha's life was marked by other tragic life events that should have knocked her out, from losing her close uncle and her father, breaking both of her feet, and later losing her beloved dog. Her strokes were another life event that could have, as she said, "taken me out or to a sad place, but being raised to be resilient, I decided to not let my strokes get to me."

"I've always been a positive person, thanks in large part to my father and mother. I believe that you can't worry about what you can't control, and you have to be OK with that. After my stroke, when I was in the hospital, one of the first questions I asked my doctor was, 'can I go to my gym and work out?' I still had a scheduled class at Orangetheory for the afternoon of my strokes, and I didn't want to miss it," Alesha said. "Maybe that does say something about me, but I think anyone who goes through a stroke or any other traumatic event has to be the driving force in their recovery. Even if you have a support system, you have to remain positive. It's incredibly easy to feel isolated and become depressed because you think no one else is going through what you're going through. This is why I wish non-stroke survivors understood that [recovery] is a process, and it isn't usually a fast recovery at all."

***

In the ensuing year and a half, Alesha has reflected on the attitudes of the paramedics and Bend Fire and Rescue staff towards her symptoms and how they overlooked things when evaluating her. She maintains that the way they approached and responded to her could have had more dire consequences for her health. "I've had friends and family advise me to maybe seek litigation in the matter, but," Alesha hesitated, "I don't know if it would be worth it, and not just because of the time, effort, and money it would take. Especially the time, but also because even in the medical field there is a perceived idea of what a stroke survivor looks like."

The stereotype of a stroke victim is that of a seventy-five-year-old person who drinks, smokes, and doesn't take care of themself. Alesha hopes to help dispel that myth not just through her story and her continued improvement of life post-stroke, but also through daily interactions.

"Occasionally when I'm working at the food truck lot, I'll be talking to a customer and the conversation lands on my stroke story. And they'll be shocked that someone like me could have a stroke," said Alesha, who doesn't have any noticeable aphasia or many physical signs of a stroke anymore. It surprised her to no end, too. "Maybe if they had seen me with a cane, but fortunately I haven't needed that for over a year now. I also wish that people knew not to be afraid to ask questions. I truly believe that huge part of dealing with anything medical, whether it's about someone's personal medical issues or someone else's, is to just learn to understand the issue."

Since the strokes, Alesha went from using the cane and worrying about drop foot to working on her feet three to four days a week. She still has a long way to go to get back to where she was before the strokes, but now her goals include self care. Rather than treating her body like a tool to be shaped and knocked around, she understands that her body requires grace and love, especially since she is still a very "go-go" person.

As far as the delays in care she experienced from various medical professionals, Alesha doesn't hold anger in her heart for them. She recognizes that everyone is fallible, even the professionals. That doesn't mean, she said, that they or the public can't become more educated on the long term or sudden signs of a stroke. What Alesha wants people to understand is that when someone is in pain, don't just ignore them. "Believe them and work with them to identify where the pain is coming from."

"It would be easy for me to be angry at Bend Fire and Rescue because of the way they reacted to my stroke. Instead, I focus my anger and frustration into positive changes," Alesha said. "And yes, even though every time I see a fire truck or ambulance in Bend, I feel that anger well up, I choose to not hold it because it's not a good thing to hold onto. Rather, I choose to remain mindful and focus on my goals and aspirations for my life."

Making positive choices like that will always connect Alesha to her father. "Even after these nearly nine years," she reflected, "I still feel a responsibility to continue his legacy."

WRITING
AND REACHING OUT

Joyce Hoffman

by Lili Alpaugh

"The stroke has given me more patience,
more empathy towards others."

Oh, no. I'm in *real* trouble!

That was Joyce Hoffman's first thought after waking up in the hospital, her son at her side, telling her she'd had a stroke. But that wasn't all. He then told her she'd been in a coma for eight days.

Joyce was sixty-one and worked as a technical and corporate trainer for Cozen O'Connor, a 500-person law firm in Philadelphia. A self-described extrovert, she loved finding novel ways to teach technical skills to lawyers, paralegals, and support staff. On the side, she wrote for newspapers and TV, and gave speeches on consumer-related topics, such as "Ten Best Ways to Approach a Company."

Joyce lived in Philadelphia, and had two grown sons who were out on their own. She was an avid runner, played the piano by ear, and led a book club which she'd started 13 years prior. She considered herself first and foremost a writer, but said, "My interests were all over the place. I was living the life!" And her health? Joyce had none of the typical risk factors for stroke, like high blood pressure, high cholesterol, or diabetes.

Joyce's hemorrhagic stroke occurred on April 8, 2009. She'd developed a terrible headache in the evening and took two aspirin, but it didn't help. At 4 a.m., she began having seizures, so her partner called 911. She became unconscious and fell into a coma. Paramedics brought her to the ER, but she was soon transferred to Capital Health Regional Medical Center in Trenton, NJ, where she would spend the next 28 days in specialty acute care.

When Joyce woke from the coma, she tried to respond to her son, but realized in horror she wasn't able to say *anything*. She knew what she wanted to say, but her mouth and vocal cords wouldn't obey her brain. "I thought it was the end of the world for me," she said. "If I couldn't talk, how was I going to live?"

***

Unable to communicate and having little information about her condition, Joyce often felt frustrated at Capital Health. She woke one day feeling thirsty, and when a nurse came into her room, Joyce pointed to her mouth. The nurse got the message and said, "Honey, you can't have anything to eat or drink. You have a feeding tube in your stomach." Joyce ran her hand over her abdomen and felt the rubber tube inserted there. She didn't realize she couldn't swallow, and that she'd choke on food or water.

It was an even bigger shock when she tried to reach for something with her right hand and couldn't do so. Her right arm hung limply by her side. She tried to move her right leg—it wouldn't budge, either. No one had told her that her whole right side was paralyzed. Joyce felt helpless and invisible. She felt a huge sense of loss, and feared the future. Soon, she became depressed.

A cantor visited her once and she tried to tell him she was depressed. He said he didn't know what to do except pray for her. A psychiatrist prescribed two antidepressants, but they didn't help, either. "I starting thinking I should call Dr. Jack Kevorkian and see if he could assist me with 'the final solution.'"

After a month, Joyce was moved to a rehab hospital. While the therapists were encouraging, she found her initial therapy slow-going, and felt thwarted by her inability to ask questions. The speech and language therapist gave her a communication board to use, but Joyce found this strategy too slow. She had to point to one letter at a time to spell just one word! She hid the thing in a laundry basket on two occasions.

She was also frustrated when the occupational therapist tasked her with putting buttons through buttonholes without explaining the benefits of doing so. When she asked why, she was told to "just do it." Her depression deepened.

"To be honest, I was not always a compliant patient," Joyce admitted. "I was impatient and sometimes refused to do what they asked. It was not like me—I'd always been such a patient person. But although I resisted at times, I never gave up. I was determined to beat this thing."

One day, five weeks after the stroke, a nurse came into Joyce's room, and thinking Joyce looked uncomfortable, fetched several pillows and carefully repositioned her in bed. Joyce felt so grateful; this nurse had noticed something that she needed, and took the time to care and respond. Suddenly, Joyce blurted out, "thank you," surprising both herself and the nurse. Joyce realized then that she *could* talk. Of all her experiences in rehab, this was the most joyful.

***

After two and a half months in the first rehab hospital, and a month in a nursing home for subacute therapy, Joyce went home.

But returning home to live with her partner of 12 years was not the happy occasion Joyce had hoped for. She could transfer herself to the toilet, to the wheelchair, and to the bed without any help, and wheel herself around using her left arm and both feet, but her right arm was still paralyzed, and occasionally she had to ask her partner for help.

She hesitated, though, because he seemed to resent her requests and often complained. This part of her recovery—feeling rejected by him—was the hardest. She ended up moving temporarily to her son's city, Pittsburgh.

While still with her partner, Joyce was consumed with depression. One balmy day in June, when Joyce was visiting outdoors with her partner's family, his cousin Elaine came and sat next to her.

"Joyce, you're a writer, right?" Elaine asked.

"Yeah…" Joyce responded, tentatively.

"So, why aren't you writing now?"

Joyce was silent, then simply shrugged. How could Elaine understand how much confidence and self-esteem Joyce had lost and how depressing it was to have only one functioning hand?

But it got Joyce thinking. If she typed rather than wrote, and put more focus on *living rather than dying,* maybe she could start writing again.

The very next day, Joyce researched how to start a blog, and the day after that, began writing "The Tales of a Stroke Patient and More," about her journey as a stroke survivor. The response from readers made her realize her mission was to help stroke victims this way, and became the impetus for her to eventually turn the blog into a published book.

Soon after, the leader of an online support group who'd read the blog asked Joyce to write a column, and she agreed. She now had purpose in her life, even if it meant typing an entire piece using just one hand, one letter at a time. Her depression soon left for good.

***

Today, Joyce lives independently in Portland, OR, close to both of her sons. A caregiver helps with bathing, shopping, and household tasks during the weekdays. She takes care of herself by staying hydrated, meditating, and doing breath work. The web site headspace.com also helps her to relax. Joyce can walk with a cane when an aide is standing next to her, using a gait belt, but for now, she uses a wheelchair for safety. Her goal is to walk using a cane by herself.

She now has her own editing business and has collected her blog posts into a book, *The Tales of a Stroke Patient,* which chronicles her recovery. "I didn't do this to make money," she clarified. "I did it to boost the dignity and self-esteem of stroke survivors."

The book's publication resulted in an invitation to speak at the Hershey Medical Center in Pennsylvania. Joyce, formerly a gifted public speaker, was terrified at first, but she followed her speech therapist's advice "to speak slowly, on the exhale, and overemphasize my words. I couldn't believe it—my speech was a hit!" Since then, she's spoken at other venues, and recently started another blog, *Dear Joyce,* which features questions written by stroke and other brain injury survivors, and answers by her and the community.

Her advice to other stroke survivors: "Don't give up. No matter how hard it seems. And don't let anyone tell you that you have a limited window in which to recover. They tried to tell me that. You'll continue to make gains if you keep working on your goals. I'm a testament to that!" She emphasizes that anyone can have a stroke, no matter how healthy or fit they are. "Know what the signs are and pay attention to them. Get help immediately."

Joyce misses running and playing the piano, but has accepted those losses. She also misses working at the law firm, but finds her current work deeply rewarding. She loves her apartment, where her office has a huge picture window overlooking a beautiful urban forest. She opens the window often to feel the breeze, smell the fresh air, and hear sounds of people talking and laughing below.

"I can honestly say I'm a happy person now," she said. "I'm at peace with where I am. The stroke has given me more patience, more empathy towards others. I realize I don't need a man to get by. I can do for myself. And I find *so* much meaning in helping others."

STRENGTH AFTER STROKE

Keith Taylor

by Jake Sheaffer

"Find a new passion to move toward. Then move that direction. Once you do this, you will be on your way to an exciting and prosperous life after stroke."

From the second-story window of his home, Keith Taylor watched the sun fall behind bright, autumn foliage while a dark, heavy cloud gathered over him. He wondered on that lonely afternoon, after his wife Babette went off to work, whether he had more value to his family alive as a stroke survivor who needed constant care, or as a deceased father with a substantial life insurance policy.

In 2010, before his stroke, Keith was proud of his purpose in life. He was co-owner of a multi-million-dollar cabinetry manufacturing business in Oregon, and for nearly two decades, he worked as its sales manager. Knowledgeable about his company's product and comfortable in his client relationships, he felt content knowing that when he sold his portion of the company, his retirement would be safe and his family financially secure.

But when he was 47, a genetic disorder called HHT (Hereditary Hemorrhagic Telangiectasia) caused a stroke that pushed his life's plan in a new direction. The first couple months of rehab were an uncharted journey, partly due to the fact that when he was discharged from Oregon Health & Science University, the staff failed to provide any of the rehab resources that could have helped him with mental and physical recovery.

"Babette had to reach out to friends who worked in the hospital to see if they could help us." His depression increased every day while he waited each afternoon for Babette to return home. When she would return, Keith's darkness and isolation would vanish, but only temporarily.

In the midst of his depression, however, a bit of grace came into his life.

"It was a couple months after my stroke, in that cloud that hung over me each day, that I thought about other stroke survivors out there and how they must be going through similar emotions," he said. "It was the beginning of an idea. An idea that included a desire to reach out to other survivors, shift my focus, and help them."

But Keith couldn't make his idea a reality yet. "I had found a new purpose, but there was still hell ahead for my wife, my family, and I."

His company asked him to move closer to the shop. They wanted to get him involved in different aspects of operations. This however, meant the end of Babette's long-standing job and the first of seven new homes in the next ten years.

Along with Keith, Babette felt anger, sadness, and frustration. For her, not only did Keith's stroke change her work life, she had to alter her social life, and come to terms with the contrasting changes in Keith's behavior.

"It's the little things," she said. "It's things that to someone else appear normal, but to me, being with him, I noticed him getting tired quicker and frustrated with putting stuff together. Even more so with computers."

But as a couple, they had something that helped them make it through. "We've always had a strong relationship, even before the stroke," she said, adding that they have always been optimistic and supportive of each other. "Many of our friends and family members complimented us on our communication, which helped to great effect after the stroke."

While Keith continued to recover and started one-on-one coaching with people and building some programs to help stroke survivors, Babette had a moment of clarity one day at work. One of her co-workers, who knew what Babette and Keith were going through, reached out to her.

"She told me about how her father survived a stroke, and how her mother felt the need to speak in place of her father. With her mother consistently answering every question and explaining what her father had felt, her father failed to identify the man he needed to be. My co-worker talked about how her father never had a fulfilled life after that. How can we have a purpose if someone always speaks for us?" Babette asked.

After hearing that, Babette knew what her goal was. "It was to help Keith heal by letting him express himself mentally and emotionally, because how can someone heal if someone else is speaking for them?"

***

Keith tried to maintain his position as a sales manager, but the stroke had affected his memory, so he would forget products, company employees, and worse, customer names. On Fridays, he and his three co-owners gathered for a weekly meeting. He found the meetings the most difficult part of his job. His aphasia made it difficult for him to communicate, which caused him to break down in tears in front of his peers, powerlessness to express his thoughts and emotions to them.

In an attempt to stay with the company, Keith transitioned from his management position to a driver with the business, but that didn't last long either, as he often found himself mentally and physically exhausted after each shift.

One Saturday morning, his partners called him in. After small talk and empty expressions of care, Keith was let go from his position with the partnership. When the partners said the company was ineligible to receive a tax incentive off of Keith's disability, Keith felt like a pawn in a chess match, and that his role was undervalued.

After Keith was let go, he and Babette found themselves in a new valley of confusion. Once again, they asked themselves, "What do we do now?" and once again, they leaned into their strong relationship to help them through. Eventually, they both found renewed energy from the unexpected release from Keith's former employment.

"It was a blessing in disguise," Keith said. "I was now able to focus on teaching, on coaching, and helping other survivors adjust to their new life." He was excited to help people see that even though they had a stroke they could still be a good parent, a great spouse, and a friend. "They just need to change their mind and start down the path of getting better."

He also wanted to help survivors find a new purpose. "When people discover their purpose, they create a plan, and from that plan, they can find renewed joy for life." He decided to form an organization, one focused on mental and emotional rehab, the kind of rehab he'd wanted after his own stroke.

Keith called the organization Strength After Stroke at www.strengthafterstroke.com

It's designed to give stroke survivors opportunities to share their emotional challenges, and to get support for processing them so they can move forward with their lives. Keith knows firsthand how many different feelings a person can have after leaving the hospital.

Anger is a common feeling after stroke, he said, adding that it's normal to feel anger towards the countless doctor appointments and the cold shoulder patients may sometimes get from medical staff who find themselves under pressure to treat as many patients as possible. Are we just boxes for some of these doctors to just check off? he asked.

Fear is another. "In some of our meetings, we talk about the fear of perception, the worry that someone in a grocery store is watching us and for some reason thinking about us," Keith said. "Some of us have physical tells when we walk, others it's in our face, and sometimes it's when we talk that we worry the stranger on the street is going to notice us and judge us."

"I remind survivors and myself that nobody is spending that much time concerned with you or your physical differences. They are concerned with their life and their goals. I tell them it's about working on yourself and about getting better with what is good for you and your family."

Depression and the morbid thoughts it creates are typical as well, said Keith. He notes that suicidal thoughts are often brought on by a loss of purpose and a lack of mental health resources. He wants survivors to know that it is possible to make peace with such thoughts.

Keith also sees value in having honest discussions with fellow survivors about how their friendships, romantic relationships, and even marriages and family relationships will change—and often times not last—in the aftermath of stroke.

He and Babette recounted the emotional distance that grew between them and close friends after Keith had his stroke. Most of the partners at Keith's company disappeared from his life after he left the business. Often, it was left up to him to make the effort, and Babette saw how much it hurt him. It's a difficult reality, said Keith, but no one is to blame for these changes and frustrations.

"Things have gotten better between our closest friends," Babette admitted, "but the physical distance between Central Oregon and the valley does make it difficult. We stay in contact with everyone, but both parties have to put in the effort and work at it."

Most importantly, Keith wants to help survivors to understand that if they are willing to work at it, they can continue to get better. "The key is your willingness to work for it," he emphasized, adding that his ability to remember words has improved due to his working at it. "Life is usually going to be different after stroke. Be open and honest with yourself about this." He continually encourages survivors to take the time they need to redefine their goals. "Find a new passion to move toward. Then move that direction. Once you do this, you will be on your way to an exciting and prosperous life after stroke."

Keith's natural ability to motivate himself was why Babette married Keith, and why she continues to love him to this day. That self-motivation is why he never succumbed to his earlier thoughts of self-harm. In a video on his web site, Keith says: "Yes, you are going to have tough times, but you're still going to make it."

***

For Strength after Stroke, Keith developed a program called "B.A.S.E." The acronym stands for belief, attitude, strength, and energy. It's a fifteen-module course that helps participants navigate and process the mental and emotional challenges stroke most often throws at survivors. Each module has a worksheet for people to engage with, and takes anywhere from five to twenty minutes to complete. Keith has plans to roll out online trainings and a Facebook support group, too.

"B.A.S.E. really helped me with developing a true sense of self-actualization. Following my stroke and the end of my business partnership, I seemed to be traveling to multiple different towns to find a new sense of belonging. But when I created B.A.S.E. for Strength After Stroke, I found a home in helping people find their foundations across the board."

Today, Keith and Babette are pleased to see the strides the medical community has made, with new advancements that have helped them identify HHT in his daughters, granddaughter, and grandniece.

Though there have been changes, including education to de-stigmatize stroke survivors, Babette tells survivors to make sure they have an advocate with them, a close friend or family member, before they get discharged from the hospital. This will help the survivor get the right information about prescriptions and other care instructions from medical staff.

Besides motivating survivors to accept their new reality and find a new purpose in life, Keith also shares the practical strategies that have helped him such as eating right, napping, and not overdoing it each day. "If I overextend myself without having a nap a few times per week, it will catch up with me. I also need to schedule myself properly. I have learned to do this over time."

The two of them hope that through Strength after Stroke, Keith's upcoming book on stroke awareness, his podcast, and both of their personal testaments, they can provide a helpful map to survivors and their families as they travel the difficult road ahead of them. Optimistic and enthusiastic at the life before them, Babette and Keith know his new purpose is set, and their family is secure with Keith by their side.

Keith is ever grateful for the love of his wife and caregiver, Babette. "We seem to live in a society where detachment is encouraged to protect us from feeling," he said. "My wife never left my side, and she only fueled my passion to help others through Strength After Stroke. To have someone to be with you through thick and thin, move to numerous houses, and just demonstrate loyalty, there's nothing more powerful than that. I love her dearly, and I can only hope that stroke warriors across the world can be blessed with such angels."

"I have a piece of advice for caregivers. Take care of yourselves first. Eat right. Exercise. Get enough sleep. Take some time for yourselves. The stroke survivor that you take care of relies on you. Stroke is a long haul issue. If you burn out, then who do your stroke survivors depend upon?"

—Marcia Moran

PROMISING FUTURE

Tom Baniewicz

by Diane Huie Balay

"You've got to work at your therapy every day at home, too."

When Karen Baniewicz got home from work on that late October afternoon in 2016, she was already anxious. Her husband Tom's court case was set for sentencing the next day. It was his second DUI and the penalty could be jail, a fine, and/or losing his driver's license.

Karen found Tom "out of it" when she entered their Naperville, IL, home. "He was just acting strange," she said, and she assumed he had taken a sleeping pill or two and possibly a drink.

"The next morning, he was still acting strange and out of it," Karen said. "Our daughter Amy and I got him down the stairs, and I decided

I'd better take him to the hospital. When we were about two blocks from the hospital, he started having a massive seizure. I drove straight to the emergency entrance and ran inside for help."

Shortly thereafter, the doctor told Karen that Tom was bleeding in his brain and that he needed surgery immediately. "He came through the surgery fine," Karen said. "He was talking to us, but in less than 24 hours he had another major seizure, and they had to operate again. This time it was a long surgery."

Karen said she didn't really grasp how serious Tom's situation was until the intensive care team put him in a medically induced coma which lasted for 30 days and eventually put him on a ventilator. He was administered the Roman Catholic sacrament of Anointing of the Sick which is usually administered to those in serious condition.

"I was either very optimistic or very naive," she said. "When the doctor said, 'I want you to think about what you would do if he has to go on life support,' I thought, 'What are you talking about? He's going come through this!'" Tom doesn't remember any of this. In his mind, he went to bed one night and woke up five weeks later in Manor Care rehabilitation and nursing home in Westmont, IL. He was very confused.

"I thought we had been on a trip to San Diego," he said. When Karen and their daughters said they had not, Tom objected. "Just pull up the pictures!" he told them, "But there weren't any pictures. We never went. It was all a dream, but it was so vivid!"

At first, Tom didn't realize how bad the stroke was, and when he did, like many stroke survivors, he blamed himself. He thought that his years of heavy drinking had caused the stroke. "Drinking got me fired after nearly 29 years on the job," Tom, a civil engineer, said. "I thought then that I was over drinking, but I was kidding myself." He got another job, but a volatile office disagreement freaked him out, he said. He started drinking again and lost that job, too. "Alcohol is the solution to everything, right?" he said, with a touch of sarcasm. "I lived for the next drink. I didn't stop until my stroke."

After the stroke, the desire to drink was gone, but other huge challenges remained. He had little, if any, control of the entire left side of his body when he awoke from his induced coma. He started therapy right away, and he listened to the therapists. Karen recalls the first time she saw Tom walk in rehab, a belt tethering him to the therapist. "I had tears in my eyes," she said. "I got stronger and stronger," Tom said. "By mid-December, I was starting to walk with a walker."

Tom had good therapists and that made all the difference. They told him, "You are going to walk out of here by mid-January!" It would be a huge victory, if it happened.

On Thanksgiving Day, Tom was alone in his room and still on a liquid diet. Liquid turkey did not appeal to him. Then Karen and their adult daughters Amy and Sarah swooped in with his favorite, a smoothie, and spent Thanksgiving dinner with him. He loved it. By Christmas, he was allowed to leave rehab briefly to join his parents and the rest of his large family to celebrate the holiday.

"Christmas was my first experience outside of the hospital or rehab. The left side of my face was still drooping," he said, "but it was cool to get out. It was nice."

True to his therapists' prophecy, Tom walked out of rehab using a walker in mid-January. Tom was happy to get home, he said, but he felt 30 years older. Although he could walk, his left arm felt like it weighed 100 pounds, he said, and he still couldn't use his left hand. Although therapy taught him do a great deal for himself, he needed a lot of help and that help was Karen.

"I was his hand," she said. "I helped him up the stairs to take his showers, helped him into the shower. I got his pills out, trimmed his fingernails, opened bottles and jars for him, took him to the doctor, therapy and hair appointments, do household repairs, shovel snow, put his CPAP breathing machine on him, adjusted his arm brace, etc.," Karen said, while still working full time as an interior designer for commercial properties. "I had to work," she said. "We couldn't afford for me not to work."

She said that Tom's personality has changed for the better since his stroke. "He's far easier to live with now than when he was drinking," she said. "That was hell! He doesn't get angry anymore or depressed, but occasionally, when he knows how to do something but he can't do it physically, he gets a just a little bit frustrated.'" So does she. "Tom's not a saint to live with," she said, "But I'm not a saint to live with, either.

"For the most part, I'm fine," Karen said, "but there are times when I've had it. It isn't often but frustration can affect both parties." She has also learned to mentally and emotionally let go of a lot, something she says her faith helped her understand. "I was in church," she said, "and it seemed that the priest was speaking directly to me when he talked about the importance of turning your problems over to God." While it hasn't been possible for Karen to let go of every single thing that she cannot change, she says she knows that eventually she will. It just hasn't happened—yet.

Tom continues the physical and occupational therapies that began in the hospital. The speech therapist made a suggestion that would change Tom's life. "Keep a journal," she said. So Tom did. He started a Facebook page to track his progress and he now has 5,000 Facebook friends, many of them stroke survivors, for whom Tom posts encouragement everyday. The journal helps because progress is slow. It can't be seen from day to day. But looking back in a month or so, progress will be obvious.

"I know because I had to start over from scratch," he posted. "Relearning everything, and I mean everything, is no small feat. But for me, it was just a matter of listening to my therapists and doing what they asked me to do. Sure, it is not easy because your brain and your body will not want to respond all the time."

Four years after the stroke, Tom can jog more than three miles, but it didn't start out that way. In a slow, planned process, he started by walking and gradually picking up the pace until he could jog from one driveway to the next driveway on their block, then walk again. It took grit and patience, but he never gave up no matter how slow the progress.

Tom believes that progress is 100 percent due to attitude. "If you don't have the right attitude, you're going to be miserable," he said. "You can't just go to therapy twice a week. You've got to work at your therapy every day at home, too. Don't worry about what you can't do, think about what you can do."

Now retired, he helps with house cleaning, emptying the dishwasher, doing the laundry and once a week he cooks dinner, something Karen highly encourages. He likes to cook, he said, but he is doing it all with one hand.

Despite the drastic changes in his life following the stroke, there were some constants: Karen, his daughters, and his many friends. There's Bob, who has been a friend since kindergarten, and Jim, who has been a friend since the fourth grade and was best man at his wedding. Others have been his friends for more than 35 years. In the past, they fished and camped and, Tom's favorite, played golf together. Since the stroke, his friends all stayed close and very supportive during Tom's recovery. They plan outings that he can do like going out for a burger or to watch a game on TV. The fishing and camping will have to wait because Tom can't do those things—yet. And that's the magic word for the Baniewiczs—yet. He may not be able to do some things, yet, but there is promise in the future.

To that end, Tom started golf lessons with the Freedom Golf Association, a national group that helps people with disabilities play golf. He doesn't know how he's going to play with one hand that doesn't work, but he's confident they will teach him. At the same time, he works diligently at strengthening his hand. He works hard with FGA, hitting ball after ball with one arm, his instructor nearby. He hopes that eventually he will once again enjoy being outside and on the links with his friends, old or new.

Tom has a new life after the stroke, one far different from his old, alcohol-fueled life that led to so much grief for himself and his family. "If I hadn't had the stroke, I would be dead from drinking," he said and he is thankful for it. Today his life is about giving hope and encouragement to the stroke survivors among his thousands of readers.

One of the posts that Tom repeats from time to time says, in part, "It doesn't matter how many times you fall so long as you get back up. Never . . . ever give up."

NO LIMITS
Angie Kirk

by Kerry Chaput

"I've never given up, and neither should anyone else."

In 1999, Angie Kirk was thirty-four and running full steam ahead as a wife and stay at home mom in Fairfield, CA. She spent her days with her five- and seven-year-old sons, Christopher and Phillip, volunteering in their classrooms, driving them around town, and helping them with their homework. She couldn't have imagined that in November of that year she would wake up in the ICU completely paralyzed and unable to speak.

On November 12, Angie was driving her boys home from a birthday party. Right before she merged on the freeway, her son told her he needed to use the bathroom. She stopped at a nearby pizza place. As they were walking back to their car, Angie felt as if butterflies were fluttering in her head. She led the boys back inside where a police-woman was on her lunch break.

Angie told the woman that something strange was happening in her head. Seeing her son begin to worry, she tried to console him, but she found herself babbling. "The scariest part was being confused and not knowing what was going on. The policewoman helped me sit, and shortly after I was unconscious."

She recalls moments in the ambulance and the emergency room, in-cluding the doctors discussing the right course of treatment. They asked her if she would like the medicine tPA which works to quickly dissolve clots. They weren't certain what had caused the stroke, and if it was a bleed, it could worsen her symptoms. She agreed to the tPA and hoped for the best. That was the last thing she remembers.

Angie fell in and out of consciousness before ultimately waking up in the ICU on a ventilator and completely paralyzed from head to toe. She could hear everything but could only communicate through her eyes. "My faith is strong and I knew God was with me. That gave me peace, and I knew I had to fight."

When her husband Phillip arrived at the hospital, Angie communi-cated to him that she didn't want him to bring the boys. "I didn't want them to see me like that." Angie says her husband was prepared for the worst. He was devastated. He wanted to help but he felt powerless and overwhelmed. He didn't know if she would make it through this, or stay paralyzed forever. Neither did Angie.

***

After 10 days in the ICU, Angie was medically stable and transferred to Queen of the Valley Hospital. "I remember seeing that sign that said "Rehabilitation" and thinking, what are they going to rehabilitate? Even the therapists were overwhelmed because I was so affected." In a month and a half, though, she would walk out of the hospital all on her own.

"I worked hard. So hard that I was exhausted every day." At first, she couldn't even push the nurse's button in her bed. "It was awful to know that I couldn't call for help if I needed anything." She couldn't eat or speak and was dependent on others for everything. But one day something happened. "As the PTs were transferring me to the chair, they felt movement in my calf and started right in working with my leg. Soon, I felt my fingers and toes begin to twitch."

Progress seemed slow, but Angie rejoiced in one tiny twitch at a time. Though she was breathing on her own and starting to move her limbs, and the speech therapist even brought her a latte when she began to swallow safely, she was growing tired of not being able to eat or walk or communicate.

Angie said the therapy was by far the hardest part of recovery. It was difficult, frustrating and sometimes painful. On top of that, Angie was in the hospital over Thanksgiving, Christmas, and New Year's just before it turned to the year 2000. "Everyone was scared of Y2K. I decided that I was going to be off all machines by New Year's Eve just in case. And I did it."

***

During her time at the rehab hospital, the occupational therapist brought Angie to a stroke support group. "I hated it," she said with a laugh. "I think I was too prideful. I didn't want others to see me like that. Maybe I didn't want to admit it to myself, either." She agreed to go, and looking back, she feels this is one of the most significant factors in her progress. "Being able to connect with others and help them through their journey helped me, too."

A month and a half after arriving at Queen of the Valley, and just before New Year's Eve, Angie walked out the front doors on her way home. It was a triumphant moment she thought might never arrive. But when she returned home, she found more challenges and frustrations awaited her. "I wish I would have listened to advice. I didn't use a walker and ended up falling several times and hitting my head. I let my pride stand in the way of safety."

Angie now uses a cane to help her with balance, something she still struggles with.

Angie said the stroke happened not just to her but to her entire family. She remembers when she was in the ICU, when her kids finally did visit, she could see Christopher, the five-year-old, terrified. "I couldn't even talk to calm his fears."

The hardest part of coming home for Angie was knowing the effect her stroke had on the family. "I learned that while I was in the hospital, my five-year-old would cry himself to sleep at night, wondering where his mom was and when I was coming back. My older boy tried to be so strong for his younger brother."

The stroke was hard on her marriage, too. "Phillip was working overtime," she said, "running our business, parenting the kids, helping me recover. He even had to teach me to drive again. He lost a lot of weight and the strain on him was immense."

The emotional strain took a toll on Angie as well. "I began to realize many years ago that I was sad and irritable. Depression is very real after a stroke." Her entire life had changed. Activities she used to enjoy no longer interested her and learning how to live life over again is exhausting and overwhelming. "I've been on antidepressants for years and it has made an enormous difference for me."

Angie had to learn to do things all over again. Speaking was especially difficult. "It would take me extra time to form my thoughts into words. When I was fatigued, my husband would grow frustrated. We both needed to learn patience and we had to learn to work around that."

Angie felt that her husband had to take on all of her struggles, sometimes wanting to do things for her, like tying shoes or opening doors. Although she was quiet and nonconfrontational before her stroke, she learned to set limits and make her needs known for the best chance at recovery.

***

What helped her and her family cope? "Support from our family, friends, and church helped us through it. It was overwhelming to see how much everyone stepped up to help us." But her biggest motivation were her kids. They inspired her to work hard and keep faith that she would recover.

It was a long year of rehabilitation and commitment that found her returning to the new normal of her role as mother. She was able to help the boys with their homework again and drive them to school.

Beyond that, Angie was surprised that the part of rehab that she initially didn't like—attending a support group—became something that kept her motivated in the long months of recovery. "I ended up creating a stroke survivors' support group. My local hospital didn't have one, so a fellow survivor and I created one." Angie found purpose through classes, giving presentations, and visiting with other survivors in varying stages of their recovery.

"My stroke gave me the grace and understanding to find moments of compassion in all parts of my life."

Since her stroke she has become a more vocal advocate for herself and for others. "God gave me a purpose. To make an impact on others and their recovery. The people I meet know that there is someone on their side. Often we are the only socialization they get outside of doctor appointments and therapy."

Angie has passed the twenty year mark from her stroke. If she has one piece of advice to give others it's that your progress can continue if you keep working toward it. "Never let anyone put limits on you." She has seen firsthand how progress can happen for years after her stroke.

"The more you put into therapy, the more chance you have of recovering." Her speech and balance continued to improve over the years. She still sees progress, even two decades later. "I've never given up, and neither should anyone else."

HE'S GOT *MORE* GAME

Jim Patterson

by Ellen Santasiero

"Rehab is a rebuilding of the information super highway.
It's a reconnecting and rewiring of your brain,
which I've learned through this process is one
of the most amazing organs ever made."

Jim Patterson stood in front of his bathroom mirror getting ready to put his tie on. It was six months after his stroke, and he hadn't yet put his tie on by himself.

He was petrified.

A lifelong athlete who played football in high school, and later golf and tennis, Jim knew firsthand that a player's mental game had to be just as good as their technical game. His stroke, though, proved to be a formidable opponent that forced him to level up his mental game in ways he never expected.

Standing in front of the mirror, he thought: "How am I going to do this?" But his next thought was: "You can do this."

"Miraculously, my arms started moving just like they used to. I tied the tie, cinched it up, and I got my collar down."

"It was amazing," said Jim, his voice catching with emotion. "I told my wife, it came back, just like my physical therapist told me it would." Jim had been working hard in therapy for months, and this was one of the first times he experienced his brain's rewiring taking over. "My left hand and left arm were very involved in tying that tie."

Jim said it was the best he'd ever tied a tie in his life "I celebrated that small victory by going through the house and yelling and laughing at the top of my lungs."

***

After a hemorrhagic stroke caused Jim to fall and hit the putting green at a golf tourney in Reedsport, OR, in 2020, his first concern was making it to an 8am tee time.

"We were the defending champs, so I kept insisting people let me get up. An ER nurse told my wife, do not let him get up, we need to call 911 immediately," Jim recalled. At a small hospital in Reedsport, a CT scan and MRI revealed a blood clot sitting behind Jim's right optic nerve. He received tPA, a clot-busting drug, and was flown to Sacred Heart Hospital in Eugene where a neurologist performed a thrombectomy.

Jim's doctors believed his stroke, which paralyzed his left side and took the sight from his right eye, was brought on by atrial fibrillation in combination with sleep apnea, high blood pressure, and pre-diabetes. "I was checking all the scary boxes," said Jim, who was 58 at the time of the stroke.

When Jim began rehab, he was blindsided by the cognitive challenges of rewiring his brain. Those challenges then gave rise to emotional and mental challenges. "My prior understanding of stroke didn't include the impacts on the brain," reflected Jim. "I was not only dealing with physical recovery, I was also dealing with mental recovery."

One of the problems, Jim admitted, was that he just didn't like what he termed "failure." When he would go pretty far with a particular rehab activity, he didn't choose to focus on what he had accomplished, only on the fact that he wasn't able to complete the activity.

Mike Studer, Jim's physical therapist, picked up on the problem right away. "He would gently provide a level of reality for me, a new reality, and say, 'Jim, don't be so hard on yourself.'"

"Even though you know you are going to make progress in rehab, simple things like walking up and opening a door are not happening the way that it used to, and so now you start thinking about the things you can't do."

Jim's mental and emotional states were also affected by his grief about losing his former self. "Our wonderful mind can also play tricks on us. The minute I started focusing on how my golf handicap used to be a 7.7 and now was a 25, it put me in a bad place."

At the beginning of rehab, Mike asked Jim a crucial question. "What did I want to get back to doing? he asked," recalled Jim. "The first thing that popped out of my mouth was I wanted to play golf with my friends. I'm not saying that that's the best thing I should have said, but that's what I said!"

Immediately after that, Jim said he wanted to be able to pick up and hold his three grandchildren, Jenny, Bobby, and Ace, whom Jim calls "Little Man." "It wasn't good enough that they could crawl up on my lap. Poppa wanted to grab them and pick them up with the physical strength that I knew I would get back. Mike immediately shifted my focus from the things I couldn't do to those things I wanted to do again."

Mike designed a physical therapy regimen to help Jim reach his goals. Some rehab challenges appealed to Jim, others frustrated him. Working with a triangular-shaped board, Jim had to put little pegs into round holes. "I hated that activity, but it was very important. The board was called 'The Conqueror.' I told the therapist, 'one day I'm gonna conquer it!' And I did! And he celebrated with me."

"Mike told me from day one, 'Jim this is not going to be easy. This is is going to be hard.' That's when I decided to look at rehab like an athlete, a pro athlete. A lot of things in my life came easy, but I knew rehab was not going to be easy. I'm going to have to put in the work."

To Jim, approaching rehab like an athlete meant drawing on some of the things he'd learned from sports: the importance of teamwork, persistence, and perseverance. It also meant stoking his inner competitive fire. "Getting well again is a competition between the old self and the new self and being the best you can be in who you are today." Perseverance and loyalty to his team helped Jim on days he wanted to skip rehab. "I didn't want to do that because [my physical therapists] were making an investment in me."

The best thing, though, about bringing an athletic mindset to recovery, said Jim, is that "you can win. Stroke warriors can be winners. We don't have to be losers. That's one of the things you pick up as part of athletic competition."

For more inspiration, Jim looked to Washington quarterback Alex Smith, an athlete he knew about from his time at the University of Utah. Smith suffered a traumatic injury to his one of his legs in 2020. Jim learned about Smith's rehab journey on an ESPN series. "His rehab was grueling and painful at times, and he spoke about the importance of keeping hope and not falling into dark places."

Too, the rehab story of gold medalist and runner Michael Johnson, who had a stroke in 2018, gave Jim hope and helped him feel less alone. "You can be the fastest human being on the planet," noted Jim, "and stroke can be a part of your story."

"To be able to listen to others' stories," said Jim, "I think this is the importance of care groups and getting together with people who have a shared experience."

Jim got constant encouragement and support from his physical therapists. "What I enjoyed most about rehab was the grace, love, and support I got from Mike and the people involved in my rehab. And they never pulled any punches."

***

When Jim had his stroke, he was executive vice president and chief communications officer for the Oregon State Credit Union. To keep his job after the stroke, he had to return to work six months later, by January of 2021. "I was motivated to get back to work because I was the one providing for the family," he said. He also needed the health insurance. But, he said, "I didn't understand how challenging that might be."

Though Jim was welcomed back warmly by his boss and colleagues, he soon recognized he couldn't perform the way he once did, especially with regard to remembering and processing information. "You can't explain why you can't remember things from two meetings ago. That's the piece I didn't know enough about before going back to work because I thought I could do anything," he said.

"What I quickly learned was even with that attitude, you will face challenges."

Jim's challenges at work affected his mood at home. "I was kind of a butt-head at times. I was short, and not as patient or considerate as I should have been. I just didn't know that the stroke would impact the way I communicated and responded to others."

In time, Jim said he surrendered his pride and embraced the fact that he was depressed.

"I needed professional help to get out of that dark spot." Fortunately, said Jim, his physician referred him to a professional counselor and psychologist, a heart attack survivor and a man of great faith like Jim himself. "He knew what this journey was about for me. I could tell when I was sitting there sharing my story, that he got it."

In counseling, Jim realized his workplace was not helping his recovery. The rest of his care team agreed. "To get fully healed mentally and physically, I had to focus 100 percent on myself. Because if I don't do it, who does it?"

Leaving his job, though, meant the possibility of Jim's not being able to work and earn an income again. At first, Jim recalled this prospect as a "scary, scary deal. But you know what? It was an important decision to make."

Jim always had strong Christian faith, and the stroke recovery strengthened it even more. By the time he made the decision to leave work, he wasn't terribly concerned about finances because he "knew the Lord would take care of me, and he did."

Three of Jim's long-time golf buddies—members of "The Beaver Posse"—who knew it would be difficult for Jim to pay his insurance premium, sent Jim and Valorie checks to cover four months, and then his parents paid for another month. Jim said that's what "the Lord will provide" means.

***

Top-notch physical therapy, counseling, and a background in athletics were not the only things that helped Jim recover. Most important was Valorie's profound love and support.

"She really reinforced our wedding vows," said Jim. "This is the 'in sickness' part of the wedding vows. What a commitment she has made to help me and stand by me in this journey."

Jim is acutely aware of the impact his stroke had on Valorie. "Her life was upended to a greater extent than mine, because she had to compensate for things I couldn't do, sometimes at the expense of things she wanted to do."

When Jim's rehab team advised the couple that Jim shouldn't be home alone, that meant Valorie was chained to the house. "She was so committed that I would not fall and get set back. She wouldn't leave me by myself until Mike gave us the green light." When Jim was recovered enough to be by himself, he encouraged Valorie to "go play pickle ball with your friends, do the things that bring you joy. She would say 'you bring me joy.' No greater love do I have for the Lord and my wife."

Jim's deep Christian faith, his family, and his friends also helped him tremendously.

Jim's and Valorie's community at Salem Alliance Church held them with love during the aftermath of Jim's stroke, especially their friends Stan and Patty Pynch with whom they attend Bible study. "During COVID, we did home churches so we could maintain those connections and relationships. We did social distancing and wore masks."

"After the stroke, my reliance on my faith and my willingness to put all my life's burdens at the foot of the cross were now things I had to actively do," he explained. "I had to surrender to God's will."

Stan, who also plays golf with Jim, reached out to their other golf buddies to help with practical needs. "I needed bars in my shower, and my good friend Roger O'Neil came over and installed them for us."

"People rallied around the two of us. That is one of the benefits of being vulnerable with your friends and asking for help. Many of my friends say, 'you tell me that you are being blessed, but I feel I am being blessed as well.' There are so many people who want to help. God used those people's gifts and talents to help us."

Jim added that men are not as quick to form deep relationships with other men, but through athletics, he has built meaningful and deep relationships. "When you spend four hours three times a week with men on the golf course, you don't just talk about golf, you talk about life. When the stuff hits the fan, those are the people who rally around you."

"One thing I had to fight was wanting to have pity parties for myself. There is no place for that in recovery for stroke warriors." Jim said it was significant that Valorie didn't let him focus on that, and neither did his son Josh, who is 28, a football coach, and a recruiting assistant for the OSU football program. "He would not allow me to stop my regimen of exercises. He drove me just like he drove his kids."

Jim said his relationships with Josh, and with his two daughters, Melissa and Katie, have deepened greatly. "When dad needed them the most, they were there." So were his brothers Steve and Mike. "They work very hard for a living, but they made a point to be at my bedside every time they could." When Jim was considering leaving his job, he was grateful to talk to his parents about it, and get their support. "I needed that," he said. "The love of family was huge."

Jim also found support from an unexpected source. "My Facebook page blew up after my wife started posting videos of my rehab. My old football teammates and my church family gave me shoutouts on Facebook. That really helped fire my endorphins and give me energy, to know that people literally across the world were praying for me in my battle to get better."

"I can't tell you how many people responded back with 'thank you, Jim for doing this' because they had either experienced something similar or knew someone in their family who had. That made the fight worth it. I know social media has been criticized, but it's been a blessing in many ways for me, because it helped me share my story."

Jim feels blessed by the stroke experience in other ways. "I became a much more empathetic and patient human being, with greater empathy for folks who battle mental illness." Having been in some dark places himself, Jim now knows the great need for people to be connected to positive, helpful strategies that relieve depression. "I can say that with credibility because I've been there."

***

A year and two months after his stroke, Jim went to a park near his home in Corvallis, OR. There he met his daughter and grandchildren, who were visiting from Sacramento. "They came for my birthday on September 7th," he said. "I was able to pick them up and walk with them." He made one of his main goals. And he has a photo to prove it!

What's more, he is back to playing golf with his friends.

"Just the very act of putting a tee down, setting a golf ball on it, and then standing there thinking how you've got to take the club back—which is going to throw off your equilibrium a bit—and bring the the club back down to the ball to hit it straight up the faraway *with sight in only one eye* ... it was my friends who said that was a miracle," said Jim. "I told them I believe in miracles. I prayed for one."

Even with those victories to his name, Jim is still working to make more progress.

In the meantime, he asks God to reveal his new purpose in life. Though he is medically retired, Jim asserts that he is "not the kind of guy whose going to sit around and do nothing."

One answer to his prayers led to his involvement with the nonprofit Stroke Awareness Oregon. With a longtime career as an executive leader with an extensive network, Jim is poised to help SAO raise funds and promote its mission in the corporate world. Jim wants to help other survivors fare better at work than he did. He bears no ill will towards his former employer, but his experience there "pointed up how very little people understand the challenges of stroke warriors in the workplace." He stresses the necessity of showing stroke survivor colleagues extra measures of grace.

"Inherently people are good," he mused, "and they don't want to hurt others, but when I knew I was falling short of expectations at work, that put me in dark places. Nobody needed to tell me I was falling short, so it felt insensitive when it was being pointed out over and over again."

"If my coworkers had been aware of my challenges," he said, "I don't think they would have taken some of the approaches they did."

***

There was one thing that Jim wasn't sure he would ever be able to do again: attend an OSU Beavers football game. In the fall of 2021, he did just that.

"This past weekend the Beavers were playing playing Idaho. I was able to walk from the parking lot to Reser Stadium, stand in a very long line, and then climb 40 flights of stairs to my seat without any stumbles or fumbles. You start asking yourself questions like 'will I ever be able to do it again?' But I was motivated to do it again. I had practiced on the 16 steps in our stairway at home."

Jim said he'd like to play pickle ball with Valorie, but that may be a stretch. "I remember the first time my brother Mike threw me a Nerf football. I was absolutely horrified when I saw it coming because I knew I had to get both of my hands up to catch it, and that wasn't happening like it used to."

***

When other stroke warriors ask for advice, Jim tells them to celebrate every small victory. "And make sure you do it with other people," he adds.

He also advises them to go through counseling with their spouse. "If you have the opportunity, do it. If you truly value your relationship with your caregiver, recognize they are going through some of those dark places, too, and they need people to talk to. We went through counseling together, and it was a wonderful thing."

For believers, Jim coaches them to put their faith in action. "From whatever walk of life or faith you follow, embrace it wholeheartedly." When his ophthalmologist told him he'd never see with his right eye again, he asked his church community to anoint him with oil and pray over him. "I've read stories in the Bible where people have regained their sight, and I said, 'why the heck not me?' I didn't take the doctor at his word. I understood physically that might be the case, but the power of prayer and miraculous healing is something I believe strongly in." Philippians 4:13 "I can do all things in Christ that gives me strength" is a verse that Jim always keeps close to his mind and heart.

For stroke warriors who have a passion for their recovery and for helping others, he encourages them to consider helping an organization like SAO. He suggests health-care providers be honest with stroke warriors about potential cognitive struggles. He said if he'd been warned about that, he would have been easier on himself when he experienced challenges in rehab and at work.

He wishes more people in the workplace realized what stroke warriors have to go through just in order to get up and get ready for work. "For me, it meant getting up really early when sleep is so important to recovery," he pointed out. "Getting dressed, getting mentally prepared. My wife literally helped dress me every single day. There were days when I thought, I just don't want to do this anymore because it isn't doing me any good."

What did do him good was focusing on the things he could do. "Mike made it clear that I was going to see signs of recovery for as long as I worked hard at it. There are people in the medical community who unfortunately don't see it that way. I don't think they realize that puts a damper on people's hope. You can't tell someone they only have two or three months to do it."

"The minute you do that, you stifle their ability to embrace a full recovery. You can't put limiting factors on the human spirit."

"There is no more long-term goal than recovery and healing and so, kudos to those of you who, like me, wake up each morning uncomfortable, but grin and greet the world anyway."

—Geoff Babb

IN LOVE WITH LIFE

Roz Dapar

by Diane Huie Balay

"You are not alone. Never give up.
Embrace the person you are today. Celebrate every
single step of progress that you make."

Roz has been a survivor since she was five years old. The strength, tenacity, hard work and even fear that helped her survive then would, years later, help her survive a stroke that would immobilize half her body.

It was 1972. From the outside, it would appear that the house by the golf course of Lompoc Country Club in California was home to an affluent family. But on the inside, five abused and abandoned children huddled in the darkness trying to survive.

Roz Dapar, age five, was the second youngest of the Asian American children.

"At first," Roz said, "we didn't understand that Mama wasn't coming back."

When they at last understood, they agreed on one thing: They must stick together. They lived in fear that Child Protective Services would separate them and put them in foster care. So, they cut and trimmed the yard at night, worked to bring in the little money they could, and ate whatever their thirteen-year-old brother Rhys shot with his BB gun— jackrabbits, snakes, frogs, or quail. They cooked on a hibachi outside.

But they had friends. Some of Roz's friends invited her to church. "I liked the Baptist Church," she said. "They had food!" Food or no, Roz found a faith and a relationship with God that would sustain her through what was to come.

Eventually, Child Protective Services did step in and they notified Roz's oldest sibling, Robin, 19. Robin was in Long Beach, CA, studying at Brooks College, a premier fashion design school. Robin left school, came home, and went to work to help take care of her younger sisters and brothers.

When Roz was a sophomore in high school, Robin's fashion design background helped her land a job at the most luxurious department store chain in Dallas, Neiman Marcus. Robin moved the whole family to Texas. This led to Roz also working for Neiman's, and eventually filling her wardrobe with stylish, expensive black. This would come back to haunt her.

While working full time, Roz attended college and earned her business degree. Neiman Marcus paid her tuition.

Marriage and motherhood followed and it looked as if Roz was surviving very nicely. Until the next disaster. In 2001, she and her husband were nearly killed in a horrific motorcycle accident. A passing stranger administered CPR to Roz until the ambulance could get to the accident site. Roz spent a year undergoing facial reconstruction and physical therapy as her marriage disintegrated and ended in a bitter divorce in 2007.

Putting her life back together with her daughter Caitlin, Roz prepared to become a substitute teacher. Her first job was baptism by fire. She was assigned to a special education class. The children in the class had a variety of the most severe physical and cognitive challenges. For Roz, it was love at first sight.

"I found my dream job," she said. She loved teaching the children, kindergarten through fifth grade, and trying new and creative ways to help them learn.

She found another kind of love, too. In 2011, she married then Air Force Master Sergeant Clay Himes. They bought a house in the Dallas suburb of Plano and put in a saltwater pool for Roz, a former competitive athlete. Roz spent untold hours creating a tropical oasis in their yard.

On the day after Christmas 2017, Clay was working at Barksdale Air Force Base in Louisiana. With her close-knit family visiting, Roz was having a great time. She was in the master bathroom while her family was in the kitchen on the other side of the house. The next thing Roz knew, with a "thunderclap headache" she was on the floor and their pit bull Bailey was licking her face. Roz couldn't get up. She yelled for help, but no sound came out. Somehow she communicated with Bailey to go get help, and the dog did just that.

When the family arrived at the bathroom, they couldn't tell what was wrong with Roz, and Roz couldn't tell them. They called Clay who told them to dial 911.

At the emergency room, Roz was improving but suffering with a splitting headache. The doctor diagnosed a migraine, prescribed aspirin, and sent her home. Clay arrived from Louisiana just as she was discharged.

Two days later, Roz collapsed by the front door. As she fell, she knew what was happening. And that was when she started yelling at God.

"It was terrifying!" she said. "I literally wanted to die. All my hopes and dreams disappeared down a black hole."

She yelled at God for 10 straight days while she was in intensive care. Actually, for the most part, she couldn't make a sound. The entire left side of her body was paralyzed.

"It was horrible," she said. "To lose control of your body is terrifying. Because my eyesight was affected, the people who came into my room looked like disembodied heads. I had hallucinations. I couldn't brush my teeth. I couldn't drink out of a cup. It took three people to get me to the bathroom. I couldn't even wipe my own butt."

One doctor asked what he could do for her.

"You can give me one of those shots," she said.

"What shot?" he asked.

"The one that puts you to sleep and you don't wake up."

She was so determined to die that she started looking for a new wife for Clay. Clay would have none of it. He rewrote their wedding vows on a large tablet and placed it on the wall where she could see it. Her special education friends were constant visitors who helped her mentally and physically. Caitlin slept by her side every night she was in intensive care.

"Without that support," Roz said, "I would still be in the bed today. Depressed."

Speech therapy started while she was still in intensive care and continued throughout her hospital stay. As her ability to speak improved, she learned that her mental filters were gone. Before her stroke, she never drank or cursed. After, "I became a comedian and cussed like a sailor. The F-bomb would just come flying out!"

When, after being hospitalized for 40 days, she finally got to go home, "I was elated!" she said. "I was so happy to see my cat litter box. I could see my garden."

She could also see her closet full of the black designer outfits she loved. She knew that was going to be a problem because she couldn't help spilling food and medicine on her clothes.

Her answer was Lilly Pulitzer, the Florida designer whose vividly colored clothes—hot pinks, oranges, blues, purples, bright greens and yellows—were often highly patterned with flowers, foliage and sea creatures. Roz could spill orange juice on her "Lillies" and no one would ever notice.

Confined to a wheelchair, she continued to have a lot of pain and aphasia as well as other physical challenges. In February 2018, she was accepted for therapy at the UT Southwestern Zale Lipshy Stroke Program. Zale Lipshy was not for the faint of heart. It was grueling.

Every day, Roz worked hard in physical, occupational, and speech therapy sessions.

"It was at Zale Lipshy," she said, "that they adjusted my meds, I overcame aphasia, and I attended Social Therapy. I became mentally sound again. I began to connect with people again and began to see my purpose again."

The hardest part, she said, was when a therapist would ask her to do something that she couldn't do.

"I cried the whole time," she said, as she attempted to do what was requested of her. "It was a battlefield in my mind."

The love and support of Clay, Caitlin, and stepson Aiden kept her motivated, she said, as well as a longing to return to her "kindergarten babies," her special needs children. Returning to her dream job would not happen. Clay and Caitlin convinced her that the job was far too physically demanding. She sadly realized they were right. She also realized that keeping their two-story dream home and her beautiful designer clothes was not an option.

They sold the house and the clothes and moved to Barksdale Air Force Base in Louisiana. Not, however, before Roz received a challenge from Caitlin's best friend, Chelsea. Chelsea was to be married the following year in Dallas. She asked Roz to officiate at the wedding and to walk down the aisle to do so.

"You've got to be bloody kidding me!" Roz stormed, but she agreed.

Roz went online and became a licensed wedding officiant. She spent the year with her therapists at Louisiana State University School of Allied Health working toward the goal of walking down the aisle. She worked with her speech therapist on what she called her "lazy tongue" to be able to pronounce the words of the wedding script.

The work was worth it. Roz was ready and able to walk down the aisle and officiate at the wedding. The day before the wedding, however, the bride changed the script and Roz had no rehearsal time to prepare. She abandoned walking down the aisle. Instead, she sat at a beautiful glass table in her flowing purple ensemble and her sparkling Keds until time to begin. Then she proudly stood for the entire ceremony. Every time the newly printed script had a blank space, Roz told a joke. The wedding was a great success.

Following the wedding, Roz rolled into her next therapy session. A group of therapists were gathered around the reception desk. They asked Clay a question. Money changed hands.

"What's going on?" Roz demanded.

"We had a bet on how many times you would drop the F-bomb," they said.

Not once. She didn't drop the F-bomb one single time.

Roz lost her dream job but she now has another: to help as many people with traumatic brain injuries as she can. As she continues her own therapy sessions in the teaching hospital, she is helping train medical students, therapy interns, and aides who work with her. She teaches them the innovations she developed for her special needs children and they try out new therapies on her. These students will go out into the world as medical professionals in an ever-expanding circle of care and rehabilitation for those with traumatic brain injuries.

Three years post-stroke, Roz can now walk with a cane and sometimes without. Little by little, feeling is coming back on her left side. Clay, now a senior master sergeant, and Roz own a home on the water in Florida where they will retire when the time comes. In the meantime, they are full time RVers.

"I love my life!" Roz said.

To those who have suffered a stroke, a traumatic brain injury, Roz said this: "You are not alone. You have a lot of brain mass left and you can recover. Never give up. Embrace the person you are today. Embrace where you are today. Celebrate every single step of progress that you make."

HER OWN MIRACLE

Diane M. Barnes

by Ellen Santasiero

"The myth of the one-year recovery comes from our system.
Most everyone has a long recovery period. Never give up.
Never stop looking for services. Never listen to
anyone who says you can't get better."

In the fall of 2005, three months after Dr. Diane Barnes suffered a hemorrhagic stroke, her phone rang. It was Steve, a fellow doctor she'd worked with at Kaiser Oakland in California. He said he'd heard about Diane's stroke.

Diane was a fifty-five-year-old single mom in San Rafael with two boys, unable to work, and sleeping 20 hours a day. Her stroke had caused aphasia and major gaps in her perception. "When I got home, I didn't even know what the sink was. I knew I had been told what it was, and what that silver arm did, but I couldn't remember."

When she was thirsty, she would go to the kitchen, but once she got there, she'd forget why she came. If she did remember to reach for a glass, she would think, "Now, what am I supposed to do with this glass?" When she first saw herself in the mirror, she ran her hands over her face and felt the piercings in her ear lobes as if for the first time. When she spoke, her words made no sense. "I didn't have any idea how impaired I was."

An occupational therapist from her employer, Kaiser, made sure Diane could live safely in her home. The therapist taught her that when she was thirsty, she was to say "glass of water, glass of water, glass of water," until she had the glass of water in hand. A speech therapist from Kaiser helped, too, but those visits were numbered. In a few months, both insurance and employer-sponsored rehab would peter out.

Worst of all, after telling the chief of neurology—to whom her primary doctor sent her for specialized care—about her ongoing cognitive challenges and that she could barely make herself understood to others, he told Diane to "just live with it." She was desperate.

On the phone, Steve asked if he could come over. Years before, he had rebounded from a traumatic brain injury from which he was not expected to survive. He wanted to see if he could help. Diane said yes.

***

Three months earlier, Diane was working as a radiologist at Kaiser, and was a devoted mother to Logan, fourteen, and Takeshi, twelve. She was fit and healthy and had no family history of stroke. While riding her horse one summer evening in the oak woodlands in Marin

County, a crushing pain in her head made her lose control of her horse. Fortunately, the horse knew something was wrong and walked back to the stables. When she got home, she went to bed, not expecting to wake in the morning.

She did wake the next day. Despite her headache, she drove Takeshi to camp in the Gold Country, much to his distress, as he could see his mother was not well. Twenty hours after the stroke hit, Diane was in the neurological ICU at Kaiser Redwood City Medical Center. Although she had some weakness on her right side, she was sent home a week later because she could walk, feed herself, and use the bathroom by herself. "But that," she clarified, "hardly makes you capable of going back to your former life."

***

When Steve arrived on that fall day, he gave Diane a notebook and pen. "He told me to bring it everywhere, and write everything down in it because he knew I couldn't trust my brain," recalled Diane. "He told me what digital organizer to get and which GPS system to get when I was able to drive." He warned her that she would feel "kicked to the curb" by both her employer and her insurance company.

Rehab would continue to be hard, he said, but the brain is very plastic. "As long as you try, you can recover almost anything." He told her she had to take charge of her rehab, and he then gave her a list of local people and resources who wouldn't turn her away.

Before he left, Steve said, "Diane, be the miracle you need." With those words Diane made stepping stones, and on them she began to walk her way out of despair.

***

When Diane's insurance and employer-sponsored rehab ran out at seven months, she started doing rehab at a small beige building on the campus of the College of Marin. It was the Disabled Students' Lab. Inside it was quiet and dimly lit, and it housed eight computers and other rehab equipment. When Diane arrived, a kind, middle-aged woman in a turtleneck and perfectly applied red lipstick led her to a computer. Diane propped her cane against the desk and settled in while the woman loaded the computer with therapeutic-quality games and programs to help Diane rebuild and strengthen her cognitive skills.

She worked at the lab three to four times a week. "They told me I was beating myself up and not to come so much, but I did anyway. I mean, I couldn't do anything else." She pushed herself because she was used to it—she was a self-described high achiever from a hardworking family, a third generation physician trained at Yale School of Medicine—but she also pushed herself for her children's sake.

"It was very disturbing for my children," she said. "Not only was I not the person they recognized, but they heard me walking around the house saying 'glass of water, glass of water, glass of water.' It was a little unsettling, to say the least." Worse, she simply couldn't parent them the way she had in the past. Logan started to make risky choices, and Takeshi, who was already at boarding school, felt abandoned by his mother. "Church and neighbors helped, but you need a village," she said. She knew the best thing for them, and for herself, was to rebuild what she'd lost as quickly as she could.

At the Lab, Diane started rebuilding pathways in her brain by concentrating on analogies and numbers and word clusters. One of the digital programs that challenged her most was a "SimCity" type game for exercising memory and visual discernment. First, she would build a city "block." "I could choose the colors, aqua, peach, something I liked, to make it easier for me to remember the block." But then the game would challenge her to recognize her block from another angle. "For me, that was impossible. I couldn't recognize it from another point of view. I cried every day with a box of Kleenex," she said. "Some days were just so hard. I felt I was beating up against a barrier that I couldn't break through. I thought, something's got to help me because I'm trying my best." She would go home and fall on her knees and cry, but the next day, it was back to the Lab once again.

Over time, she improved. The aphasia resolved at around seven months, but she still had challenges with vision and fine motor skills. Besides using the digital programs, coloring "tessellations"—patterns of shapes that fit together with no spaces or gaps between them—in Lab-issued coloring books helped her sharpen these skills.

A year after her stroke, Diane went back to work at Kaiser two hours two days a week. "If I had waited longer, I would have lost the job," she pointed out. Being back at work made her eligible for an impaired-physician group at Kaiser led by a psychotherapist. "It was very helpful to be with other doctors," she remembered.

Two years after her stroke, Diane had made enough progress to "graduate" from the Lab. Towards the end of her rehab there, she joined a support group at the Schurig Center for Brain Injury Recovery, a non-profit, post-acute therapeutic center in Marin that serves the brain-injured community over the long haul, after their insurance runs out.

"They were great," said Diane. "It was a group of people from all walks of life." She felt encouraged right away because she could see the progress she'd made in two years of mostly self-directed rehab—she could follow the stories the group members told! Moreover, at home she was able to make a grocery list and find it, and start taking down some of the sticky notes the occupational therapist helped her put up around the house. Schurig Center staff suggested she get some therapeutic games to work on at home, such as Adventure Inlay, which helped her work on visual processing speed.

Diane could also see her progress at work, but she was still slow. "I was impatient with myself and others were, too." By this time she was working six hours four days a week. "I was running on fumes. And there were still days when I was down on my knees crying." On top of this, Diane was trying to support her son Logan, who continued to struggle.

In 2006, Diane lost her mother. Once again, she fell into despair.

"I needed a new approach," she reflected. When she shared her despair with the psychotherapist at Kaiser, he gave her the name of a place in Sausalito where he thought she might reach the next stage of her healing and recovery.

***

When Diane stepped into the Center for Attitudinal Healing, she found a big, sunny room filled with couches and chairs, shelves stuffed with books and audiotapes, and a bulletin board fluttering with notices. "It was a homey place that looked like a Thomas Kincaid painting, only with California style," she quipped. On a retreat at the Center, she felt enriched in a way she hadn't experienced before. "The promise of spiritual living was so great. It felt like that was something I had missed. It was wonderful."

After the retreat, she trained as a support group facilitator at the Center and decided to facilitate the support group for those living with HIV/AIDS. That group resonated with her. "We all had a silent nonvisible disability and a major life event that had reoriented our thinking." Diane co-led that group for nine years. Around that time, she made another important decision: after four years of trying to perform well at work, she decided to leave radiology, and Kaiser, for good.

One day, Diane opened her mailbox and found a continuing education catalog from Stanford, her undergraduate alma mater. She saw a course that appealed to her. "Show Up for Your Life" taught people to use the tools of improv to live more spontaneously and in the moment. Diane had always been creative, mostly as a silversmith and sculptor in her spare time, but improv was something completely new.

She looked at the catalog and thought, "Why not? Why not just say yes to things?"

***

After taking the course, Diane was invited to perform in a play. That led to acting lessons and over time, a realization: "Memorizing lines was like rehab," she said. After landing a few more roles, she had another realization: "In rehab, I was getting better and that was wonderful, but I had something else to do now." On her decision to leave rehab, she reflected, "I wasn't so much quitting rehab as I was re-engaging with life."

Diane eventually became a Meisner-trained actor and, inspired by solo performers, decided to write and perform her own one-woman show. She began to write the story of her son Logan's struggles, but over time she saw she was really writing the story of her stroke. Her disability was inseparable from his experience. Also, she was doing more than just writing a story. She was also recreating herself—the former doctor was becoming a playwright, actor, and storyteller.

Working with director David Ford at The Marsh Theater in San Francisco and collaborating with other writers and actors, Diane wrote and performed "My Stroke of Luck" which premiered at The Marsh in 2016. She performed the critically acclaimed show at festivals nationwide, and in 2017, the show was selected for the Los Angeles Women's Theater Festival, United Solo Fest, and the Atlanta Black Theater Festival.

Diane's second one-woman show "Not One of Us," opened virtually in 2021. The show explores systemic racism including health-care equity. Due to COVID, she now performs both shows virtually.

***

In a radio interview in 2019, Diane revealed that before her stroke, she was intellectually intolerant, impatient, type A, and competitive. "Now," she said, "I have more humility, empathy, and a sense of oneness. I have so much more connection to other people." Her stroke awakened her to the reality of those who can't express themselves when they want to. She experienced firsthand how the world doesn't easily accommodate such people.

"I've gained things and I've lost things. I now listen to audio books and I need a GPS. I'm a different version of myself." She also talked about how certain memories would come back and she would see them and interpret them differently than she had before. "It was freeing to have the past unmoored from my judgements and assumptions."

What motivated her most during the dark days of rehab? Being a mother. Diane's sudden disability and the demands of her long recovery threatened to destroy her family, but she was committed to be there for her sons again. Together, she and her sons worked to heal and rebuild their family. As it turned out, they built it into something even better than before.

***

In December 2019, Diane spoke with a group of stroke survivors in the Bay Area. She heard that many of them had been told they probably couldn't—or wouldn't—get better. "I was appalled," said Diane. It was the very same thing she was told fourteen years earlier. "The myth of the one-year recovery comes from our system," she tells stroke survivors. "Most everyone has a long recovery period. Never give up. Never stop looking for services. Never listen to anyone who says you can't get better." She also advises survivors to remember that nonprofits play a huge role in awareness, treatment, recovery, and support.

While she would never choose to have a stroke, Diane has called her stroke experience "gloriously transformative." Though soul-breaking at times, her experience and resulting growth forced her to recalibrate every aspect of her life, emotionally, psychologically, and with regard to how she defines success, from the strengthened relationships with her sons to a new and thrilling vocation. She has not only redefined success for herself, but, she said, she has enjoyed success beyond her wildest dreams.

"When I talk to stroke survivors I tell them, if you compare the way things are with the way things were, you will be constantly disappointed. I tell them your old life is gone, dead. But, that's OK, you've been given a new one and you are in charge of your recovery. You have to look at it that way, and if you take charge of your attitude, you can change your life. I tell them to throw away the old rulers, relish your new life, and don't measure it against the way things were."

—Ralph Preston

IN GOOD REPAIR

Deborah McMahon

by Glenda "GG" Goodrich

"I don't like to bother people with my needs,
but I learned I do need to ask for help."

At 2 a.m. on a weekday in June 2013, Deborah McMahon woke up
hot and sweaty with a horrible headache. She took some ibuprofen,
put an ice pack on her head, and went back to sleep on the couch. The
next morning she looked in the bathroom mirror and was shocked to
find her eyes going in opposite directions. Deborah could barely see.
One eye tracked to one side, the other eye to the opposite side. She
knew something was seriously wrong.

"I consider myself a fairly smart person, but when I walked downstairs to the guest bathroom to get Advil for my headache that night, it never crossed my mind I was having a stroke," she said.

The next morning Deborah went to a clinic for a myriad of tests. There had been a bleed somewhere deep in her brain, close to the area that controls the eyes. Her doctor was perplexed. His advice: go home and rest. No rehab. No treatment. No prognosis for recovery. Deborah did not know whether she would ever see normally again. She was fifty-four years old.

Before her stroke, life was rosy for Deborah and Bob McMahon.

Both had successful careers, Deborah as a land use planning consultant and Bob as an electrical engineer. They were at the point in life when they could afford to make some of their dreams come true. They built a beautiful home on 20 acres, "a labor of love" Deborah called it. They designed the house together, chose just the right site, and oversaw the building process. When the house was finished, they finally had their dream home tucked into a Ponderosa pine forest with two horses, Eleanor and Newt, two cats, Max and Tilly, and Deborah and Bob. They celebrated with a trip to Europe.

Then, in June of 2013, Deborah had her stroke.

Deborah had no other symptoms from the stroke, but having her vision taken away was, as Deborah described it, "the worst thing." In the weeks that followed, unable to read or watch television or do anything that required visual acuity, she laid low. She immediately got herself on a good vitamin regimen and started eating a healthier diet. She rested and tried to stay positive and avoid stress.

"I think a sense of denial was my saving grace," Deborah said. "I didn't want to think about being more or less blind for the rest of my life. I tried not to go down that pathway because it was one step away from becoming very dismal."

Every day she told herself, "don't worry, say positive," but deep inside Deborah was petrified. In those moments hope for recovery was a long shot, but she didn't stop trying to convince herself otherwise.

Deborah was still working, although she was hardly able to see, and unable write. If she covered one eye and turned her head to the side to look out of the other, she could see a little, but that was a strange way to interact with people at work. She chose, instead, to memorize her presentations and count on her memory and work knowledge to get her by. Deborah's physician wanted her to wear a patch. "I'm not vain," she said. "But it is unusual to see a woman with an eye patch. The staring didn't bother me, but I think it made others feel uncomfortable. I hated that patch."

Instead, Deborah would hold onto her husband's elbow when she had to leave the house for appointments and more testing. After eight MRIs they still never found the exact area in her brain where the stroke occurred because they could not see the exact location of the actual bleed.

Deborah was adjusting to her disability and rebuilding her life when, 30 days later, Bob also suffered a stroke. He had gone out early to feed the horses and when he came back, Deborah knew something wasn't right. Bob was mumbling and she could just barely make out that one side of his face was drooping. Because of her own recent experience and research she'd done about strokes, Deborah knew immediately what was happening.

She popped an aspirin into Bob's mouth and called 911.

When Bob came home from the hospital, Deborah was still struggling with her own recovery. Thanks to help from her dear friend of 30 years, Sue Stoneman, she was able to make it through. "Sue was like a sister to me," Deborah said. "She provided both physical and emotional support for both Bob and me." It was a vulnerable time for a couple who had been together for 27 years. Bob suffered from aphasia and Deborah could barely see.

They had both always been self-sufficient and capable. "I don't like to bother people with my needs," Deborah said. "But I learned I do need to ask for help. It's not a time for stoicism." She let Sue into her private world, and trusted she would accept all the granular, unpleasant things that go along with illness and disease. Deborah continued to focus on staying positive, leaned on Sue, and navigated taking care of herself and Bob as best she could with minimal sight. Bob worked hard on physical therapy and his own recovery. Together, piece by piece, the couple began to repair the foundation of their individual lives and their forever-changed life together.

Miraculously, right after Bob's stroke, Deborah noticed a slight improvement in the realignment of her vision. After the stroke she had a nystagmus in one eye, a condition where the eye shifts quickly back and forth, and that had settled down and improved a little. Deborah was surprised and thrilled. In those first couple of weeks progress was painfully slow, like watching a pot of water boil. She had to force herself not to look in the mirror and test the progress of her eyes four or five times every day. Gradually Deborah's vision improved.

In three and a half months from the time of her stroke, miraculously her vision was almost fully restored.

Deborah considers herself extremely lucky. Now she has 20/20 vision with her glasses. Working as a land use manager for the city of Redmond, OR, she runs a complex department and is responsible for a large team. Deborah feels her stroke has made her a better manager—more thoughtful, compassionate, and sensitive to the needs of others.

She's responsive to her employees' needs during COVID, allowing them to work from home whenever possible.

Deborah and Bob's marriage is even stronger now with better, more open communication. They had experienced a serious car accident together in 1993, and their strokes brought back sad memories of that time, but they navigated this adversity like they had back then, with faith and perseverance. They had worked as a team to build beautiful home together. Now, they would become even closer as they continued to build their life together after their strokes.

During the COVID pandemic the couple has been working at home and are together 24/7. Deborah in her management job, Bob in part-time electrical engineering. Together, they are traveling and enjoying their beautiful home. They hope to be able to ride their horses again soon. In two more years, they will both retire.

Deborah and Bob have learned what is most important to them in life: being together and enjoying life. "A lot of couples don't make it," Deborah said. "It is a testament to how close we are now. We can get through this stuff."

Deborah is an active member of Stroke Awareness Oregon and helps spread the word about "FAST," an acronym used by the National Stroke Association and the American Heart Association to educate the public on detecting symptoms of a stroke.

One thing Deborah is adamant about: if a person has any symptoms, they shouldn't be afraid to dial 911. "Don't worry about overreacting; don't think you can guess what's going on," she advised. "Women have different symptoms with a stroke, and I think they don't want to be a bother," she said.

She talks about the body as the home we live in—a place we need to know well, respect, and keep in good repair. She wants people to be aware that certain health issues may crop up at certain ages. And because stroke can present differently from person to person, Deborah advises everyone to get to know and understand their own body.

"Then you can recognize when something's off. Be mindful and get help right away. Don't be afraid to dial 911."

THE BIGGEST HEART

Ralph Preston

by Ellen Santasiero

"Acceptance does not mean rolling over and
giving up. It means dealing with the reality
you have to deal with."

With his right hand, Ralph Preston slides a chunky blue rubber band
onto the thumb and index fingers of his left, stroke-affected hand.
He is seated at his dining room table in Murrell's Inlet, SC, his hand
resting on a cream-colored woven placemat.

Opening and closing his hand with the rubber band on his fingers, he
explains, provides resistance that helps him build strength. He does
several extensions with each finger before going to the next.

Ralph demonstrates this exercise in a one-minute, self-produced YouTube video. It's one of some 60 videos he made demonstrating the rehab exercises he's done in the years since his right side hemorrhagic stroke in 2008 when he was fifty-eight. Ralph is not a professional physical therapist and he is quick to remind everyone of that, but after his experience in rehab, he thought it might be helpful to other stroke survivors to share the exercises and concepts that helped him most.

A lifelong videographer and still photographer, Ralph calls himself a "communicator," and so it's not surprising that the videos are professionally produced and get right to the point. Ralph speaks clearly and simply, and breaks down every movement into steps so people at the beginning of their recovery can follow. "People like the videos because I don't talk. It's not about me. I just want them to know what to do. I just share the exercise and try to put it in context."

Each exercise is low-tech, allowing anyone to take part using common household items such as rubber bands, putty, clothespins, and a hammer, or by holding onto a kitchen counter or a deck railing. He is always thinking about the viewer and how they may need to modify the exercise based on their readiness. For example, he demonstrates how to do toe raises while sitting in a wheelchair even though he is no longer using a chair himself.

Besides the videos, each week Ralph visits around five survivors in his local community and does physical therapy with them in their homes. To date he has helped 13 local survivors in this way. He also picks up prescriptions, drives people to appointments, and shares his experiences and technical knowledge through blogging, speaking, and in support groups. Through his Facebook groups, Ralph provides virtual support to upwards of 4,500 followers every week.

He just finished raising money for a stroke survivor on a limited income who needed a new car. "There are 150,000 survivors who need a new car. I can't fix all that," he said, but in his appeal to his Facebook followers, he wrote, "I know I can't change the world, but together we can change Linda's world."

Why does he give so much of his time, energy, and expertise to the stroke survivor community? Sure, he has the communication and production skills necessary to deliver content to a lot of people, but there are other reasons he decided to serve his fellow survivors.

***

A self-described former hippie, Ralph wears a ponytail and a turquoise bead necklace. Before his stroke, he was a lifelong athlete who hiked, biked, and ran. He loved gardening, seeing butterflies in the wild, volunteering for Habitat for Humanity, and spending time with family.

In 2008, he lived with his wife Deborah in a small town in the North Carolina mountains. He was working as a video technical director on the road and as a cameraman on day shoots. Before his stroke, Ralph had high blood pressure and he opted to try to control it with healthy eating and regular exercise rather than take prescription medication.

One day, just as he was finishing a forty-five-minute ride on his stationary bike, he noticed something strange. "My legs didn't want to go around any more. I got off the bike and tried to walk. I lifted my left leg eight or 10 inches off the ground, way too high. When I tried to adjust it, I dragged it on the ground, then too high again," he remembered. Like most cyclists, Ralph's hands would get numb. "The right one started coming back, but not the left. I took a sip of water, and my lips were numb. I noticed it in my arm and leg, too. I called my doctor and told him I just had a stroke."

In the neurological unit at Mission Hospital in Asheville, NC, he and Deborah learned that Ralph's stroke was caused by his high blood pressure. "I didn't listen to my wife," he admitted.

After five days at Mission, Ralph was transferred to Care Partners, a rehab hospital in Asheville. One of the first things he did there was ask his wife to bring him one of his cameras. Some yellow Japanese roses on the hospital grounds had caught Ralph's eye. "I took photos as soon as I could," he said, though he could only use one hand. " Photography helped me cope right after the stroke."

He spent 17 days at Care Partners. Every day there he participated fully in two physical therapy sessions, two occupational therapy sessions, an arm and hand class, and pool therapy. Ralph wanted to get function back in his left side so he could get back to doing the things he loved. But in those early weeks, he couldn't even touch his nose. The day before he left Care Partners, he realized his life would be different after stroke, but not necessarily worse than before. Before he left, he told a nurse, "I'm going to be the best new me I can be!"

And then he was sent home.

He went from 42 therapy sessions a week to just four. "I lost all my sources of information," he recalled, "and I had one zillion questions." Now that he was no longer an inpatient, he figured he'd be imposing if he called one of the therapists more than once a week.

"At the time of my release from CarePartners, I lived an hour and a half from their facility in Asheville, and I couldn't drive for a few months, so getting back there was not easy. That ruled out participating in any programs they might have had and left me with rural outpatient physical and occupational therapists. And there were no rural stroke doctors per se."

So, the day after Ralph got home, he got busy.

***

Ralph wanted to learn how to set himself up for the best possible recovery. To that end, he spoke not only with physical and occupational therapists, but also with his family doctor, an internist, a blood pressure specialist, an orthopedic surgeon, his neurologist, a counselor, and a psychiatrist.

He pushed himself to do therapy 12 hours a day, seven days a week. He used up the physical and occupational therapy sessions he had coming to him, but mostly he did rehab at home. Ralph said that when he was at Care Partners, the staff preached "involvement" with the affected hand. "That's not an easy thing if you can't pick up anything or use your arm."

First, to rebuild range of motion and some strength in his shoulder, he held a light weight by his side and drew circles with it clockwise and counterclockwise. To build up strength and coordination in his hand, he squeezed putty and stretched rubber bands.

"I also did a lot of wrist-strengthening exercises with a hammer when I was just sitting around. When we went shopping, I walked around the big box stores, rather than sitting in the car or at home." Shopping carts, he added, make excellent walkers for those who need a little assistance. "Everything is an opportunity for therapy."

He kept those common household items—the putty and clothespins, the rubber bands and hammer—in the car so he could do occupational therapy while his wife drove him to appointments. "When I got home, on the fifth day I told wife I was scared of the wheelchair. She asked why. I said because the longer I sit in it the more of chance I have of getting stuck in it."

Deborah suggested they put it in the laundry room. "I started crawling and wall walking," said Ralph. After a few weeks at home, he walked a bit on his favorite beach, but he knew he had a long way to go.

Once he got some function back, he could start to think about involvement. "I began by getting the vitamins out of the cabinet with my left hand. I had trouble doing it, so I'd get them all down and then put them back. Get them down and put them back."

Ralph said every time he has trouble doing something, he does it over and over again until he is satisfied he's doing it right and he has strengthened neural networks. "I never quit. I always complete the task. I believe in brain patterning – psychological as well as physiological, and that success leads to more success."

Ralph was challenged by what he called "running out of brain." "I first discovered this when trying to regain speed. I opened and closed my hand as fast as I could. After a few times, I could feel the effort it took in my brain on the opposite side from my stroke." When he asked his neurologist if it was a good thing for him to push his brain, he said he thought it was.

"I run out of brain when I engage in physical activities using my left side. The more I complicate things, the more likely it is to happen. So, if I stand on a ladder holding a stake and a level with my left hand, lean over and pound it into the ground with a sledgehammer, I will run out of brain fairly quickly."

When he runs out of brain he feels woozy, and that his visual world is spinning. "I stop, shake it off, and go right back to it." Another thing that caused him to run out of brain is when his entire field of vision was moving. "One example is if I stood on the edge of the surf with the incoming and outgoing water filling my field of vision."

He said he had several other challenging moments. "They all involved me breaking down because others couldn't understand what I was going through." But he got through those hard times. "I found attitude was key and it took some effort to maintain it." Ralph describes himself as spiritual, but not religious.

In August, he went back to the beach and did a favorite walk to the jetty and back. "After the jetty, I decided to do another of our favorite walks to Siler Bald to see the featherbells. After the jetty, I knew I could make it."

From the parking lot, Siler Bald is a 2.5 mile walk and it rises to 1,500 feet. "We used to make it in 50 minutes. We walked it that August day in 60 minutes. I was shocked that we made it that quickly."

As he sat on top of the mountain eating lunch that day, Ralph could sense that his hard work was paying off. "I felt on top of the world. I knew then I could do most anything I set my mind to in my recovery. I knew that even if I recovered no more, I would have a satisfying life. That had been a big concern of mine as I sat in a rehab hospital in a wheelchair."

At five months out, Ralph was able to do a photo shoot for Habitat for Humanity with a heavy camera. His hard work was paying off, but he said that the next month, the six-month anniversary of the stroke, was really hard. "I thought about the anniversary in terms of how my life had changed. You tend to remember what you used to be able to do, not what you can do."

Six months later, at his one year anniversary, his attitude had changed. "I decided to celebrate my first anniversary." He marked the day by taking photos on a beautiful day. "As a photographer, I wondered about my ability to take pictures like before, and I'm referring to mentally. The challenges of movement were pretty evident that day. I didn't know if I'd be able to get up off the ground."

He took one of his favorite photos that day, called "Redbuds and Scooters." "I had an overwhelming sense of the beauty in this world and that everything would be OK with me." That was one of his most joyful moments.

Another joyful day was when he took his mountain bike to the beach and rode it 12 miles. "It was the first thing that I had done where the stroke didn't overpower the experience. I could ride like I did before!"

***

Right from the beginning, Ralph wanted to help others. Why?

"I am trying to be the person that I wish I could have talked to after my stroke," he said.

"Everyone gets sent home in their car to reinvent the wheel for themselves," he pointed out, adding that each year 800,000 people in the U.S. have a stroke. "This is illogical. We need better information and resources for those in stroke recovery, so they don't feel lost and abandoned." Since he had been making interactive videos since the early 80s, he thought, "I could do something about this with the video camera."

Early on, Ralph had plans to create a DVD for stroke survivors to use after they came home from the hospital or rehab to help them take charge of their recovery. The project morphed into the series of YouTube videos. Most demonstrate exercises, but some are motivational, and others focus on legislation affecting survivors such as the Family Medical Leave Act.

As soon as he could, Ralph began helping other motivated stroke survivors. He describes the people he helps as "those who have accepted that the cavalry is not coming and that they are responsible for their own recovery."

Besides the videos and the practical support, Ralph also hosts weekly Zoom conversations with high level stroke survivors. Ralph and his guests try to provide a "stroke roadmap," to viewers, one that covers "the basics of what you need to put your own program together. This week we had a conversation about pool therapy, and one about training, and one about how people who are athletic sometimes do better."

When asked how to get the most out of a physical therapist, Ralph tells survivors about how he always asked his therapists for homework. "They gave me things that I wasn't good at. I would go home and practice until I was good at it. When I came back able to do it, they knew I did my homework and they had a different attitude about me."

Asking for homework, Ralph said, is a good way for survivors to take ownership and responsibility for their own recovery. "No one gets better doing an hour or two a week at PT and nothing at home." He adds: "Attitude is key to recovery. Without a good one, you won't feel motivated to do all the hard work necessary to get better. Remember, it's a marathon, not a sprint."

Over the years, Ralph has thought a lot about acceptance and what it means to him as a stroke survivor. "Acceptance does not mean rolling over and giving up. It means dealing with the reality you have to deal with."

***

Ralph said that for most of his life he chased the dollar. "I was off-the-charts intense pre-stroke. I believe the stroke mellowed me some."

Serving others was modeled for Ralph growing up. "Thank you, Mom," he said, putting his hand on his heart and tearing up. "She taught us to live by the Golden Rule. I have my mom's big heart." But the stroke made him open his heart and put her teaching into action.

"I'm probably more sympathetic than I was pre-stroke. It's not that my personality changed. I just became more aware of the struggles going on around me."

For the future, he hopes he can help survivors for a long time. "You tell me something better to do and I'll do it. There isn't anything better than helping people, is there?"

Healing

happens in spirals,
    in circles, yes,
circles that grow wider,
    open, make more space

happens in spirals of skill,
    to assess, discern, intuit
and act   yes, skillful work
    that creates more space

happens in circles of wise ones,
    practicing Chi Kung, Tai Chi, yes,
giving acupuncture, massage, and cranial-sacral
    adjustments, revealing more space

happens in spirals, where
    full hearts meet brilliant minds, yes,
spin together to puzzle, ask and answer
    tough questions,
allow more space

Healing   happens
    in spirals
        yes   circles that open
          spirals make space

—With thanks to Vicki, Jennifer, Barbra, Joan, and Michelle

by Monza Naff ©1999

A MEDITATION ON RECOVERY

Kim O'Kelley-Leigh

by SAO staff with Kim O'Kelley-Leigh

"You have no idea what's coming. It's a big unknown,
but I was determined to make a full recovery, and
take the journey with joy."

When you step inside Kim O'Kelley-Leigh's home, the first thing you
see is a console piano, its keys a little yellowed, its finish slightly worn.
Arranged on the top are photos of Kim's family, along with a portrait
of Paramahansa Yogananda, and a cassette tape player. In a sunroom,
a fish tank burbles. Two parakeets perch in their cage by the window
and a tabby stretches out on the floor.

Kim's fingers twist slightly at odd angles when she stretches them and she walks with a pronounced limp—all due to the massive hemorrhagic stroke she suffered six years earlier at the age of fifty-eight. Yet there's a rhythm to her gait. She moves with confidence and purpose.

In her twenties and thirties, Kim flourished as a professional actress, dancer, and singer, but left show business when she had a daughter and decided to stay at home to raise her. Mostly self-taught, Kim had learned to play the piano as an adult, and as her daughter, Kyla, got older, Kim taught her to play. Soon she was teaching piano, singing, and songwriting to other children.

***

Three days after Christmas in 2014, Kim and her extended family had gathered at her cousin's when she felt an intense pain in her head. She excused herself and went upstairs to meditate. Half an hour later, she rejoined the others. Suddenly she felt the life force drain out of her left arm and leg, then the left side of her face began to droop. Her family shouted, "Call 911!" Kim then slumped down in her chair and vomited. In less than an hour from the time she had gone upstairs, she was in the emergency room. The neurosurgeon informed her husband that she was alive and even though she'd had a brain bleed, she wouldn't need a cranial shunt. While it was too early to know the full effects of the stroke, the doctor stated she'd have quite an effort coming back from this.

***

In the aftermath of a stroke, the acute care stage is a time of uncertainty. "You have no idea what's coming. It's a big unknown," Kim said, "but I was determined to make a full recovery, and take the journey with joy. "

After a week at Providence Saint Joseph Medical Center in Burbank, CA, Kim was transferred to the Burbank Healthcare & Rehabilitation Center, a facility across town from her home, just over the hills from Hollywood. Working with a physical therapist, Kim was informed that the stroke had caused her to be paralyzed on her left side. She immediately responded, "Paralyzed? I'm not going to affirm that."

After several weeks, Kim was able to get out of bed and into a wheelchair, and by the end of that first month she attempted to walk for the first time. With her arm in a sling to prevent it from separating from her shoulder and her foot unable to bear any weight, she held onto a bar and inched her way along a platform with her physical therapist behind her. Then the progression of exercises began in earnest; trial, testing, failure, repetition, improvement, success, followed by a new task, a new objective, and a new challenge.

Seven weeks after the stroke, Kim returned to St. Joseph's Medical Center for two weeks of intensive therapy. During this time, Kim graduated from a walker to a hemi cane—the one-handed walker designed to build strength. With a new physical therapist, Kim now faced her greatest challenge as she stood at the bottom of two long flights of concrete stairs. She made it to the top, but when she turned around and looked back down, she froze.

"Going down felt like cruel and unusual punishment," Kim recalled. "My PT reached out to take the cane and I started crying. I fell apart. No words. We didn't talk. My PT simply waited. It went on for a long time. Then she said quietly, 'You can do it'. I did my best to meet the fear of falling and moved through it. When I reached the bottom safely, there was a tremendous feeling of relief coupled with a new awareness that this was going to take everything I had."

***

When Kim went to see her neurologist for the first time after going home, the neurologist told Kim she was asking too many questions and she should go home and let her husband think for her. "I was furious," Kim said, "It sounded like she was telling me to give up. I wasn't going to let the stroke take my spirit."

At home, with the help of a new physical therapist, she set out on a rigorous program of rehabilitation. While she relied on her husband and daughter to do what she couldn't do yet on her own, they never hovered over her. "Mom you can do it" was Kyla's stance. "What they gave me," Kim said, "was the room I needed to make my own choices and to go at my own pace. They had faith in me." In addition to her family, Kim had her long-time practice of Kriya Yoga to undergird the healing process.

Working on her own between physical therapy sessions, Kim pursued her recovery. "I had the intuition that I needed to get down on the floor . . . babies crawl as their brains develop," she said. "That's how I started, by trying to crawl. My arm was too weak, but this was a good attempt because I was on the floor doing things with my body." As a dancer, Kim knew her body. "You have to keep stretching and stay flexible," she said. By the end of the first year after the stroke, she was wearing lace-up shoes and learning to walk with a cane.

At Burbank Rehab, Kim had worked diligently on her left hand and fingers to get back as much normalcy as she could. At home, one of the drills was to stack plastic cones into a pyramid on her dining room table. "That took me twenty minutes the first time I tried," she recalled. "Twenty minutes!" But as she persisted, she developed more dexterity. "Eventually I was able to stack them easily. Recovery, they say, is about specificity and repetition."

One day, she and Kyla decided to make deviled eggs. Kim could take a hardboiled egg in her left hand and chip off the shell with her right.

"Kyla and I couldn't stop laughing," she said. "Who knew you could get so much pleasure out of peeling an egg?"

***

Around the two year mark, Kim was wearing a brace and speed walking on a treadmill three or four times a week. She also joined a water aerobics class. In the class, everyone else was kicking, twisting, and peddling hard as the dance music played. Kim couldn't do every exercise. "It's not easy to have a body that . . . I was a dancer. I was an actress. To lose all that was rough. People were feeling sorry for me. I could feel it." One morning, overwhelmed by the loss of all that she'd once had and was able to do, she stopped. As she began to cry, she turned away from the others, took a few deep breaths and reconnected with her inner truth—to accept every moment with gratitude and return to the here and now, where peace and joy reside. "I remembered I was exactly where I was supposed to be," Kim said, "and everything was in perfect order."

Kim's meditation practice was crucial to her recovery, but it wasn't the only thing that helped her through. When she was young—singing and dancing on tour—drugs and alcohol began to run her life. She eventually found her way into a 12-step program and, at the time of her stroke, had been clean and sober for 31 years. "I know it would have been different had I not had the experience of turning my life around in that first recovery," she said. "It fueled me for this."

As Kim's functional competence developed, the focus of recovery began to shift, to her emotional and mental health. This was a time that involved what she called "sheddings."

"Once I had my stroke and had physical limitations, I became aware of where I was paralyzed mentally and emotionally. I'd put a lot of things off. In a way, that's a paralyzation. You want to do something and you don't do it. You put it off. My third year, in almost every meditation in the morning, I would cry. I had all this regret. I started going through all this 'what I could have done,' 'what I'd missed,' 'why had I held back?,' and 'now I can never do it'. I just started having all this regret, but it happened in the softest place, in meditation. I would weep, and then I'd turn my regret into action by getting on the treadmill or on the floor for stretching. I've moved through a lot of feelings." Also in that third year, Kim and her neighbor began writing a two-woman play, based on their lives separately and together.

Kim still wears a brace as needed, but also walks in laced-up shoes, due to her continued weak ankles, with and without the cane. She's stronger, faster, more coordinated, and more confident. She can turn around easily. She can climb the stairs in her house. "I can extend my arm," she said. "I can raise it, lift weights. I can grasp and release. I can wash and braid my hair. I can drive again."

In 2016, Kim, with another stroke survivor, started a stroke survivors' group that continues to thrive. Recently she finished compiling "A Story of Hope," a 12-minute video that chronicles five years of her recovery, and in 2020, just before COVID hit, production began on her play, "Freedom off the page."

***

Hanging on the wall next to Kim's piano is a slotted wooden box that holds a collection of cassettes going back through the decades. One of them is already in the player. She clicks the player on. It's October 2020, almost six years after the stroke, and as the opening riff takes off, she places her hands on the keys and settles into the beat. The song she's chosen? "Against the Wind," Bob Seger's ode to loss and endurance.

STILL LEADING THE WAY

Debra E. Meyerson

by Dana Clark-Millar

"Don't give up on your ability to do something
that is meaningful."

For Debra Meyerson, having two strokes in the space of a few weeks
was bad enough, but it led to another trauma that arrived full force
three years later.

It was then that Debra, a sociologist and tenured professor at Stanford University's Graduate School of Education, learned that she had
reached the end of the policy-allowed medical leave and she had to
give up her position at Stanford.

Up until that point, Debra and her husband Steve presumed that one day Debra's life would get back to normal. It would just take a lot of hard work in speech and physical therapy—which she had been diligently doing. But the University's decision forced the Bay Area couple to acknowledge for the first time that Debra's life—and Steve's—was not going to return to what it was.

"I have no idea what I am going to do," Debra recalled thinking. "That put me into an identity crisis."

An opportunity awaited her on the flip side of that crisis, though, one she would explore and develop during the first decade after her strokes. But first, she had to navigate the emotional waters of a stroke-affected life.

***

Debra's stroke journey began in September 2010. She'd just dropped off Adam, her middle child, in Boston to start college. Debra, Steve, and their two other kids, Danny and Sarah, traveled from their home in Menlo Park, CA, to Lake Tahoe for the weekend. On the drive, Debra noticed her right leg felt weird. Later, while out on a hike, her leg would buckle when she'd climb up or down. They gave up on the hike and returned to the condo where Debra took aspirin for a mild headache.

The next morning her headache was worse. Steve noticed her right arm moving slowly as she reached out for the aspirin and he saw she was having to concentrate to get her fingers to pick up them up. Steve made the connection—right leg, right arm, headache—and off they went to the hospital, even as Debra tried to convince him they should just go home and deal with it there.

At Tahoe Forest Hospital in Truckee, a CT scan showed she'd had an ischemic event. Debra was then taken by ambulance to Renown Regional Medical Center in Reno where an MRI confirmed a stroke.

At 10 p.m. that night, Debra's speech was clear but awkward, she was exhibiting some confusion, and her problems moving her right arm and leg were becoming more obvious. By morning her right side was almost completely paralyzed and the right side of her face drooped. By 8 a.m. she was mute. When Steve looked into Debra's eyes, though, he could see she was still there.

Debra was transferred once more, this time to Stanford Hospital, a world-class stroke center near her home and support network. She was in the ICU there for two weeks.

A week after Debra's initial stroke, an MRI showed no new strokes but healthy brain tissue around the original stroke site continued to die. The main artery carrying blood to the left side of Debra's brain had developed a tear in its inner lining. Doctors didn't know why it happened nor could they assess the likelihood of it happening again.

Three weeks after her stroke, Debra was in her fourth hospital, Santa Clara Valley Medical Center, in their inpatient Acute Rehabilitation Program. Before leaving Stanford Hospital, she could make some noise. The therapist at Valley Medical Center explained how speech is controlled on the left side of the brain, Debra's now damaged side, and rhythm and melody is controlled by the right. He used songs such as "Happy Birthday" and "Row, Row, Row Your Boat" to help Debra produce some words. He then created a tune for her to sing, "My name is Debra Meyerson." He chanted it over and over, swinging her arms to it. On the third try her voice joined in with his. She was able to say her name again!

She also could walk down the hall with support. The doctors thought she'd be ready to go home in a few more days.

But one morning, Steve noticed that words she could speak the day before were now garbled. A CT scan confirmed another stroke and Debra was moved back to Stanford. She hadn't lost any of the physical strength or movement she'd recaptured, just some of her newly regained speech function. This second stroke occurred in one of the main speech centers of her brain, and was caused by a blood clot that had formed behind the same flap of tissue that caused the first stroke. Additionally, Debra's blood pressure dropped and her platelet level plummeted, forcing a move back to the ICU.

The doctors recommended a stent insertion into the artery leading to Debra's brain. This would hold the flap of tissue against the artery wall. After much deliberation, Steve and Debra agreed to surgery.

The operation was successful and Debra returned to rehab at Valley Medical Center.

Though Debra was profoundly shaken, she still believed that a discrete period of rehab and recovery would result in a return to her former life. Surely, she thought, I'll be back in the classroom for the upcoming semester.

***

Debra's right leg and hand were affected, but it was her loss of speech that threatened her sense of identity. "Lying in the ICU at Stanford Hospital," she wrote, "a frequent thought for me was that life without speech would be no better than life in a cell."

She had long been an independent, active woman who hiked, cycled, and sailed. She had a rewarding full-time academic career and a rich family life. That's how others knew her, and that's how she knew herself. It never occurred to her that this identity might be taken from her. Because after all, if she wasn't that woman, then who was she?

She hit rehab hard. It included speech, physical, and occupational therapy three times per week, and Debra's days often included 30 to 60 minutes of stretching her arm and leg. She Skyped daily with her mother to work through speech exercises and she used Rosetta Stone to relearn English. "I wanted to do more and move faster. Three hours a day didn't feel enough … so I practiced as much as I could," explained Debra.

Even though she was working hard and making progress, Debra was frustrated by the gap between her desire to speak with and to others and her inability to do it. At year three, when she simply didn't have enough speech back to return to her job, and her medical leave was up, Debra was certainly angry about losing her job. But she also felt an even more powerful emotion.

"Deb compares the feeling she had when she lost tenure—that recognition that her old life was gone forever and she had to build a new one—to the feeling she had when her dad died very prematurely 18 years earlier, a heart-wrenching loss," Steve explained.

Debra's new reality forced her to ask herself some important questions. And she began to answer them during the five-year process to write—with help from her son Danny (co-author), Steve, and others—*Identify Theft: Rediscovering Ourselves After Stroke,* a book that came out in 2019 from Andrews McMeel Publishing.

***

Debra came to accept that certain parts of her former career were gone forever. But if she could understand what lay beneath her deep love of her career, she thought, she might be able to learn how to replace it with something else.

The first question she asked herself was: what do I value most about my life?

Besides cherishing family relationships, Debra derived enormous pleasure from being a professor and a creator of knowledge about the social issues of diversity, gender, and identity. Once she identified these core values, she then asked herself, how can I live out these values? Could she still teach and create knowledge, even if she wasn't a professor at Stanford?

Debra was still drawn to researching, writing, thinking, and collaborating with others—the same skills she'd always used as an academic.

Those desires yielded two of Debra's most pivotal moments.

In May of 2014, Debra stood up and addressed a small group at a gathering of social science academics called the May Meaning Meeting. It was the first academic event she mustered the courage to attend after her stroke and with her limited speech. In a twenty-minute talk she revealed her idea for a book she wanted to write, one that would help other survivors with the emotional journey to rebuild a new identity. She told them how scared she was to try, given her current limitations. But they were inspired by the idea, strongly encouraged her to go for it, gave her some great ideas, and helped her commit to the project. Five years later, *Identify Theft: Rediscovering Ourselves After Stroke* hit the shelves and airwaves in print, audio, and e-book forms.

Debra described the significant assistance she needed to put the book together—her team consisted of an outside editor and each member of her family—and although needing that level of teamwork was uncomfortable for her, it led her to states of joy and gratitude as an author that she may not have experienced with more independence.

The second came as the book was nearing publication: Debra realized she could continue to bring her considerable intellectual and interpersonal skills to bear on the field of stroke recovery. There was research and writing to be done, new knowledge to be created, and a stroke survivor community to share findings with and support. Moreover, she had firsthand experience with stroke, and she'd already been doing research on her own behalf. She and Steve decided to create a nonprofit organization called Stroke Onward where they could develop, gather, and share life-enhancing stroke-related information for others. Launched in 2019, the organization aims to "provide stroke survivors, families, and caregivers with more resources to help them navigate the emotional journey to rebuild their identities and rewarding lives."

At nine years out from her strokes, Debra reached her goal to find meaningful work to replace her former career. She could still do the things she loved—research, generate new knowledge, teach, and make a difference in the world. She didn't need to be at Stanford to do those things. She didn't need any university to do those things. She could do them elsewhere—she just had to adapt and do them differently.

***

In her journey to build a new identity, Debra used traditional therapies, but to stay on top of her mental and emotional game, she looked for help in a place she'd always looked: the social science research she had studied, and used—and helped create—for decades.

There she learned the importance of proactively choosing how we speak about our life experiences. For example, she could choose to see her stroke experience as an opportunity for growth, rather than an unmitigated loss, or as a reason to overly fixate on a past identity. Debra said this proactive approach was key in helping her move forward in a positive way.

She does feel loss and despair at times, but she works to remind herself that she has a choice about how she frames her stroke experience.

Helpful too was a concept developed by organizational theorist Karl Weick, a colleague whose work she featured in her 2001 book, *Tempered Radicals*. Weick described the benefits of "small wins."

Small wins, wrote Debra, "are little victories that have a large impact on how we perceive our situation." When we set small goals and meet them, we feel good, and feel motivated to go onto the next. Debra said her tendency is to focus on how far she has to go, and get discouraged by that. But this research helps her dial back, focus on a small step, and not get overwhelmed.

Beyond embracing information gleaned from empirical studies, Debra forced herself to interact with her support network: friends, people at the Pacific Stroke Association, other survivors, and her family. This was particularly important because people with a communication disability like aphasia often tend to isolate themselves.

"Just by living her life, by giving talks, by meeting with people, that in and of itself is speech therapy," Steve said. It reflects a "Life Participation Approach to Aphasia" (LPAA), an approach promoted by a growing number of professionals in the speech therapy and aphasia treatment community. "By participating in life and taking risks and putting yourself out there, doing what is uncomfortable because it is not what you are used to doing, that leads to more improvement, particularly for people with aphasia."

"One of the challenges of aphasia is that big projects are really hard. It is just daily frustration because of how difficult it is to communicate," said Steve.

For Debra, her thoughts are as fluid and lucid as ever, but when it comes to speaking, aphasia has left her with halted and choppy speech as she searches for words. A short sentence may come out perfectly clear, but sometimes she will get stuck on a word, not finding the one she wants. It helps that she now works with her husband Steve, who knows her so well. When she can't find the words she is seeking, she often looks to Steve, or he'll sense her frustration and ask, "want help?" With her "yes" reply, Steve can often complete what Debra was struggling to vocalize.

Steve was and is Debra's biggest champion, but the aftermath of her strokes hasn't always been easy on their marriage. For help during difficult times, the couple uses tools they learned from counselors in the past. Debra now knows how important it is to support Steve's need for time and space for his own self care.

***

Ten plus years after the strokes, Debra continues to improve, though not as fast as she'd like.

Rehab was, and still is, a daily effort involving countless hours.

She'll spend 15 minutes a day meditating, a practice that calms her and helps her rest, then 20 to 30 minutes stretching. Some days she drives an hour to a physical or occupational therapist. With modifications done to her car, a left-foot gas pedal and a knob on the steering wheel, Debra can drive herself. Thrown into most days is between half an hour to an hour of extra therapy-related exercises. She frequently reads aloud with her mom on Zoom. Walking in the hills, riding a stationary bike, or riding tandem with Steve bolsters her physical and mental health.

When she's not doing rehab, her time is spent on e-mails, maybe a Zoom talk, working with Steve creating a new presentation, or working on current projects for Stroke Onward.

Among their many activities with Stroke Onward, Debra and Steve write a bi-monthly column about the emotional journey in stroke recovery for the American Stroke Association web site and Stroke Connection newsletter, they facilitate online support groups for survivors and care-partners through Virtual Connections, and work closely with an organization called Aphasia Access, through which speech therapists committed to supporting people with aphasia collaborate to develop and share innovative approaches to treatment and support.

In 2022, she and Steve hope to ride across the country, raising awareness about stroke along the way, particularly about the need for survivors to reconcile their identity with their disabilities and build a rewarding new life no matter what.

"We just really wanted to make a difference on the issue of this emotional journey after stroke and this really is what Stroke Onward is all about," Steve explained. "It is a very different career than Debra used to have, but it is one that reflects her capabilities, her unique situation, and gives her the same kind of meaning that being a professor at Stanford did, developing and sharing knowledge to help people," said Steve. "We hope our work will help other survivors find life transitions that enable them continue to build fulfilling, rewarding lives."

That notion of not giving up on your ability to do something meaningful, and trying to find what that is for you in the face of whatever disabilities you may have, is a message that is embodied in Debra's experience. Through her work at Stroke Onward, she hopes to develop new resources and change the caregiving system so that more survivors of stroke and other traumas can successfully navigate that journey.

"If I don't look at the positive every single day, I'm going down the wrong path. That doesn't mean I didn't feel bad. Some days I didn't want to exercise. I still did my workouts every day, though. Over time, those exercises became easier and I felt better. In essence, exercising through the tough days got me in a frame of mind where I was always thinking of the positive thoughts rather than the negative ones."

—Marcia Moran

A WARRIOR'S GRACE

Ron Lusk

by Lili Alpaugh

"We are *stroke warriors,* not just stroke survivors!"

Ron Lusk will tell you that before his stroke, he was "the guy."

Back then, he would tell you that he knew more than you and that he was always the boss and decision maker. His imposing physicality and gregarious nature would immediately draw you in and make you a believer. His actual success as an entrepreneur spoke to the truth of his claims.

For most of his adult life, Ron led teams to form a slew of successful businesses, mostly large scale commercial developments. He was skilled in idea development and raising capital, and he had made a lot of money. He worked out regularly, rode a Harley, and enjoyed golf and tennis in his spare time. He was at the top of his game and loved his life.

All that changed in early November 2017. At home in Bend, OR, he was having dinner with his wife Wendy, and his longtime buddy Ryan. They sat for hours enjoying the meal Wendy had cooked, chatting, and reminiscing. When they finished, Ron stood up and suddenly realized he couldn't walk. Wendy and Ryan helped Ron get into the car and Wendy drove him to St. Charles Medical Center.

At the ER, the doctor told him he was having a stroke. Over the next couple of days, Ron's symptoms only got worse. His face drooped and he lost most of the movement on his right side as well as the ability to swallow. Neither he or Wendy knew that a stroke is not a quick event. It often evolves over hours and even days. It was hard for both of them to watch him lose function, not knowing how bad things might get or what the end result would be.

Ron learned he'd suffered an ischemic stroke in his brain stem. A small clot had formed in an artery there. He was unable to receive the clot-busting drug tPA due to a number of medical factors. Not every stroke survivor is a candidate for that treatment.

Ron spent about a week in acute care at St. Charles, but he doesn't remember much about his time there as he was cognitively impaired. The staff fed him through a feeding tube so that he wouldn't choke or aspirate into his lungs.

At the time of the stroke, Ron was sixty-two and had been training as a body builder, planning to compete in the Master's Division. He was bench pressing 250 pounds and could bicep curl 60. But when he started inpatient rehab and tried a bicep curl, he was shocked. He could only lift eight pounds.

In order to get his strength and mobility back as quickly as possible, Ron made a decision. "The therapists and staff were great," Ron said. "They helped me to progress rapidly. But I knew I had to work as hard as possible, so I added extra exercise to my day." He worked out with weights in his room in addition to his regular therapy sessions.

Ron worked especially hard on regaining his ability to swallow. It wasn't long before he progressed from the feeding tube to drinking thick liquids and eating pureed foods, but he had to eat very slowly and swallow twice after each bite. "A normal five minute meal took me half an hour to eat!"

One of the most helpful things to him in his recovery was his men's group from Alcoholics Anonymous. Ron had been sober for decades and had made real friends in AA from years of attending and speaking at meetings. Those friends came through for him in big ways: they offered to hold AA meetings in his hospital room, they visited him repeatedly, and they offered every kind of support imaginable.

Ron didn't find the hospital support group very helpful. "I needed to be forward thinking and not stay in the doldrums," he said. "It's true you'll go through cycles of depression. I went through that. The key is to stay focused on your goals."

A cheerful surprise occurred one weekend when Wendy snuck their new Labrador puppy, Wilson, into the rehab unit. What a joy it was to have Wilson clumsily cavorting about with his long legs and big ears and paws! He got up on the bed and stayed right next to Ron. Ron was comforted and refreshed by Wilson's spirit and devotion.

Returning home after a month in rehab, Ron used a wheelchair because it was not yet safe for him to walk on his own. He spent a lot of time resting on the sofa. Wilson sensed something was not OK with Ron and laid next to him constantly on the sofa pillows. Ron said,

"Wilson has grown up either in bed or on the sofa with me. He still lays across my chest even though he's now 70 pounds!" Wendy noted that the cushions on the sofa have been destroyed. "But who cares?" she said. "That dog took care of Ron!"

Once Ron was home, Wendy jumped into the role of 24/7 caregiver. "Wendy has been amazing. She certainly rose to the occasion," Ron said. "But I have to say, the stroke affected everything. It's changed my entire world."

There were challenges in dealing with his business partners and others who now treated him differently. "They assumed that because I had a stroke, I wasn't as capable, and they tried to compensate for me. They tiptoed around me and at times acted patronizing. It's true I was less able, especially at first, and they could see I was depressed on top of it. But I wanted to show them just how capable I actually was! My worst case fear was that they would force me to be bought out for pennies on the dollar. I've seen that happen before! I must say, though, they did go out of their way to include me, and I so appreciated it."

His two sons seemed to distance themselves from him, perhaps, he speculated, they had a fear of losing their father. As Ron said, "Maybe they didn't want to be on the trail with me if I died."

His marriage was also affected. "There used to be a balanced dynamic between us, and our sex life was wonderful. But when Wendy had to take on the caregiver role, and I became so needy, things changed. The lust and passion were gone. It's something we're working hard to regain."

Wendy was a big motivator for Ron to get up and get moving. "I used to think her frequent suggestions were a little diabolical: 'Hey, you wanna go for a walk? Hey, see if you can work out extra time in the PT gym! Hey, why don't you take Wilson for a walk?' But now I'm enormously grateful that she pushed me like that and wouldn't settle for her husband laying around and becoming an invalid."

Also early on, Wendy got the idea to play games with Ron. He suggested backgammon, something they'd played together in the past. Every morning, right after breakfast, they'd pull out the game and play. "We'd play best of seven," said Ron, who estimated that so far they've played some 15,000 games. "At first I won all the time, but Wendy got really skilled and now she throttles me!"

"I have to watch her closely because she cheats! I call her on moving certain numbers that she knows is against the rules. 'You can't move that number!' I tell her. But we're totally playful about it. It's getting us out of the caregiver-patient dynamic and we're beginning to rediscover the good parts of our marriage again." The couple have since moved onto cribbage.

Ron considers himself lucky in that his abilities returned fairly quickly, but he also credits himself for working hard to get there. "Wendy helped me to get off the sofa. I had to overcome unrelenting fatigue every single day. But I began to push myself and take ownership of my own recovery. I turned an upstairs room into a gym, and found a personal trainer who knew how to modify exercises to increase the connections from the brain to the muscles. I've made progress because of that."

Ron also uses high grade, effectively dosed CBD (with no THC), which is known to decrease inflammation and heal brain receptors.

He's had other medical challenges since the stroke, such as a fall that resulted in a wound on his right foot, which became infected. While in the hospital for that, he was given the wrong antibiotic which caused his potassium to spike and resulted in a heart attack.

At this point, Ron faced his own mortality head on. The conversation in his head went like this: "God, I'm yours. If it's my time, take me. But until then I'm going to do everything I can to keep going, and I'm going to revel … just revel in life every day!" He said, "It was at this point I let go of control completely. I found I could let things go more easily and just be in the moment."

Ron made it through that frightening event and continued to recover. Unfortunately, with his foot, the infection kept coming back, and eventually he had to have the foot amputated. He now wears a prosthesis, and can walk fairly well on even surfaces, but his balance and sensory input have been affected so he has to be very careful. "I haven't gone back to fast moving sports because of that. I work out with weights, play golf, and I ride an electric bike. The ebike has been so freeing! I live near the Deschutes River Trail and I often ride along the river, in and out of the trees. Wilson often runs alongside of me. Riding on trails in the forest feels so good to my body and mind—it's like meditation on wheels! And now I bike 12 miles round trip every day from my house to downtown Bend. I keep the assist level on the bike light so I get a good aerobic workout. If things get too challenging, I just increase the assistance."

Ron helps his local stroke community as an advocate and mentor to others. When he started working with people, he made a few discoveries. One is that most people don't know much about stroke or disability in general, and that the public needs to be educated about it. "People are afraid of what they don't know," he reflected.

He added that our society needs to include people with disabilities more than it does. "Usually there is a lot that we can do."

"People need to be less self-centered. We need to take care of our limping caribou, like a herd would take care of their limping caribou. We as a society need to value service to others and helping your fellow man, not leaving him to fend for himself without adequate resources. People will discover that serving others will do a whole lot for themselves, not just the recipient, and it'll be a lot more rewarding than just staying focused on how much money they have, or on their own personal problems."

Ron noted that he speaks with authority on this. "I was a hard driving, competitive kind of guy myself. I was pretty arrogant: *I* owned the business and *I* made the decisions. Then suddenly, I couldn't contribute as before. The stroke was humbling to me, it brought me down several pegs. Today I have grace for others, a much deeper understanding, and more patience. And I want to give back."

He feels strongly that while the rehab experience was great, the discharge planning needs to be expanded. Stroke patients need a complete support system when they go home, including extensive coaching from other stroke survivors, education about all available online and in person resources, suggestions for alternative therapies, and nutrition information. They need advocates and caregivers besides their main caregiver at home, because that person needs support and respite, too.

Ron also believes that therapists and doctors should not tell stroke patients they only have six to 12 months to recover and then they'll plateau. "That's not completely true. Sure, the first year is when you can make the most gains, but recovery continues, even if it's at a slower pace. People need to know this to stay inspired and keep working toward their goals."

To new stroke survivors, he says, "Acceptance of your new normal is key to coming to terms with what's happened to you. You have to own it. You must become your own advocate and be accountable to available resources. We are *stroke warriors,* not just stroke survivors!"

MAKING A COMEBACK

Steve Boatwright

by Lili Alpaugh

"There *is* a future for stroke survivors. We don't have to feel
like outcasts. All of us can do *something*."

It was a sunny, bluebird afternoon in July 2014 when the Soul Benders
took the stage at Summer Fest in downtown Bend, OR. After band
members took their places, longtime lead singer Steve Boatwright
hobbled on stage with his cane. For the first time in his life, Steve was
afraid to be on stage, worried that he would disappoint. He took his
seat on the stool out front, adjusted his microphone, and looked out
at a sea of faces—it was an audience of thousands.

As Steve settled himself and studied the crowd, he saw they were smiling and waiting with eager anticipation. They looked so happy. That, it turned out, dissolved his fear. The band launched into its opening number, and Steve jumped right in with a voice strong and clear, and the crowd swayed and clapped and sang along with him.

Steve belted out song after song and by the end of the set, the band knew the concert was a resounding success. For Steve, the cane and the stool had become invisible. No one there would have guessed that just one year before, Steve had suffered a stroke.

***

Steve had worked in careers ranging from the electronics and radio industries to music and even gymnastics. In 2008, he took early retirement and moved with his wife Pam from the San Francisco Bay Area to Bend where the population was smaller and the air cleaner. Steve and Pam opened up Elite Repeat, a high-end clothing consignment shop where they worked alongside dedicated volunteers every day.

But what Steve enjoyed most was singing.

Prior to his work in electronics, Steve toured professionally as a singer-drummer for over two decades. He signed with Columbia Records at age fifteen, and went on to play with Santana, Buffalo Springfield, Janis Joplin, and Chuck Berry, among others. After moving to Bend, he and a few other musicians formed Soul Benders, and he became its lead singer. They played classic rock and soul at festivals and concerts, and quickly became one of the area's most popular bands. "I knew I'd always sing in a band," he said. "I wasn't going to give that up in retirement!"

One evening in June 2013, Steve felt out of sorts. "I went to bed thinking I'd feel better in the morning. But when I woke up, my right leg felt heavy, my right arm was droopy, and I couldn't use my right hand. I called for my wife and she rushed me to the emergency room."

Steve had suffered a cerebellar stroke and spent the next month in St. Charles Medical Center in Bend. His first two weeks, spent in acute care, were a blur, but he does recall feeling terrified as he lay in bed. "I couldn't help but wonder what was going to happen to me. I wasn't sure if I'd be able to walk, write, or even take care of my most basic needs. I was riddled with anxiety at the thought of it all: How will my family and friends react? Will I be a burden? Will people accept me this way?"

He had no idea how the future would play out, but through prayer and his lifelong habit of positive thinking, he managed to allay his fears. Each day when he woke, the first thing he'd say was, "Thank you! I'm still here! I have today!" He could speak, but he wondered if he could still sing. He dreaded to think what life would be if he couldn't.

A nurse stopped by his room one morning and asked, "How're you today, Steve?"

"Okay," he said. "But, I'm wondering … can I sing to you?"

The nurse, taken aback at first, said, "Sure, I'd like that."

Steve then started singing "Listen to the Music," one of his favorite Doobie Brothers songs. When he realized he could produce the same tone, quality, and control that he'd had before the stroke, he was elated. He'd remembered all the words, too.

"That is *really* good," said the nurse. "You can SING!"

"Thank God I can still sing!" said Steve. "Thanks for letting me sing to you!"

***

As soon as he was able, Steve began rehab. He had right-sided paralysis and balance issues; he could walk, but only with a lot of assistance. One of his occupational therapists would have him stand, walk 10 feet, then turn around and go back while she timed him. "At first, I was slow because I was afraid of falling, but after a couple months, my time improved quite a bit. That gave me a lot more confidence."

After acute care, Steve was moved to a studio apartment downstairs in the hospital, which was part of his rehabilitation. It was designed to be a simulation of an actual home environment. He spent two weeks there, practicing independent living skills, learning how to transfer himself, wheel himself around, dress and bathe, and retrieve things he needed. His wife, Pam, also learned how to best help him when he needed it. It was great therapy for getting him back home.

The most difficult therapy for Steve was at the rehab gym, where his therapist would place him in a balance and vestibular training booth. The floor inside the booth moved, and he had to keep his balance while standing on it and keeping his eyes fixed on various pictures. It made him dizzy and nauseated, but amazingly, he progressed quickly, passing every test in the booth with flying colors. At one point, his therapist asked, "Wow, how'd you do that? How'd you recover like that?" Steve then revealed that he'd been a champion gymnast when he was younger. He'd won four state championships in a row in California and made it to the Olympic trials. "Balance, to me, was everything. I knew how to counterbalance certain movements – my body remembered."

His happiest moment came when he returned home. Still in a wheelchair, Steve noticed his little dog Zoey following him everywhere, never letting him out of his sight. She waited for him and watched his every move, and Steve was so touched by her concern and unconditional love, it helped him heal.

Steve continued his therapy as an outpatient. After hearing about a therapy pool at a local clinic, Steve made an appointment, and before long, he was working regularly in the 98-degree saltwater pool on its underwater treadmill. "I highly recommend a therapy pool," said Steve. "I found it extremely helpful both with my walking and my stamina." He strengthened his legs and increased his stamina even more by riding a recumbent bike. "The different resistance levels for me were the key," he recalled.

Steve describes himself as a man of faith, and "never a quitter." His belief in God gave him the strength and confidence that he'd make it through the challenges ahead. "On days when I just didn't feel like going to therapy, I would immediately tell myself, you're not a quitter, you are stronger than your opposition in every situation."

"I see every day as a gift, a new opportunity to get better and improve." He's noticed and celebrated every improvement that has come along, no matter how big or small. "You can't think that the new movement in your finger is 'only one tiny inch', you have to think of that inch as a *milestone*. Because it is!"

While his "can do" attitude has certainly helped his recovery, Steve is honest about the difficult times. "Sometimes you *do* fall apart and lose it, but each day you can get up and try again. And you surprise yourself sometimes in the evening, when you look back at the day and see all the things you actually *did*. Sometimes I was surprised at how much energy I'd had."

***

After three months, he discontinued using the wheelchair because he could walk independently with a cane while wearing a brace on his right ankle. He began to regain movement in his right arm.

Today, seven years after his stroke, Steve can raise that arm to shoulder level, but he still has to use his left hand to write and do other activities, and occasionally has to ask his wife to help with things, such as opening a jar. "I hate to have to ask her for help," he said, "but it hasn't been a problem for her and she never complains. Pam's been amazing!" He plans to do more therapy for his right hand.

A sense of humor has helped Steve cope with his new reality, too. He said he jokes with his grandchildren about his poor handwriting. "Hey, look! I was writing at the third grade level, now it's up to sixth grade! They said 'that's awesome. Soon you'll be able to graduate!'"

After a few months at home, Steve slowly returned to working at Elite Repeat. He was excited to be out of the house and visiting with others, but he missed singing. He contacted his bandmates, and asked them if they would help him try singing lead again. They said yes.

***

He was nervous at first, but he was never one to back down from a challenge. When the group set up for his first practice, he grabbed the mic and dug into each song they played, his voice a little weaker than before the stroke, but he had good tone and control, and he remembered all the lyrics. He was back. He could tell. All of them were thrilled.

He kept practicing with the band, working on strengthening his voice. Then came the triumphant concert at Summer Fest. He recalled, "I realized I had my life back at that concert. I had regained a purpose, doing what I love." What Steve likes about singing to audiences is that he can take them away from their troubles, at least for a time. "I know each and every person in the crowd has something going on in their lives, something they're dealing with, and they can forget all that and just enjoy the music."

Steve's advice to other stroke survivors? "It's a tough road ahead, but you must keep looking ahead and be thankful you're still alive. It's not always easy, but it's always a choice. Your choice." He said survivors have to be willing to ask for help. "You have to accept what you can and can't do and ask for assistance when you need it. Most people don't mind at all, in fact, they *want* to help you.

He also urges survivors to stay in the present moment. "Don't analyze the past. You won't be doing what you used to do. Just accept that and move on. There *is* a future for stroke survivors. We don't have to feel like outcasts. All of us can do *something*."

The pandemic of 2020 forced Steve and Pam to close their shop, but they are already mulling around ideas for what they'll do in the future. "I want to help and encourage people, that much I know. Maybe it will be through motivational speaking and podcasting," said Steve, "and of course, I plan to keep singing!"

"Give yourself a beautiful life in spite of what came out of nowhere. I can either make the best of it, find my joy, and live in my happiness, or I can be miserable, but I don't choose that."

—Kim O'Kelley-Leigh

TAKING CARE OF BUSINESS
Alan Wick

by Ellen Santasiero

"You have to get professional help from a therapist in a style that suits you. It doesn't matter what technique they use. Find somebody where there is trust and chemistry, somebody you can say anything to, and you won't be judged. Spend the money. Get professional help. It's crucial."

Entrepreneurs hire business coach Alan Wick for the depth of his experience. After all, that's what makes him good at what he does.

But Alan's success today also stems from a transformative experience he had far from the business world, one that happened in Charing Cross Hospital in London, where Alan lay for 10 days during the summer of 2016, not knowing if he would live or die.

He had had a stroke, but it went undiagnosed for almost two weeks.

It was in those uncertain days, hours, and minutes, the Thames flowing by just two blocks from his bedside, that Alan made a decision that would forever change his life and his work.

Doctors eventually reported that Alan had a vasculitic stroke caused by chronic squeezing and thinning of the blood vessels in his medulla.

The good news, however, was that he would live.

***

The son of successful business owners and investors, Alan jokes on his web site that his first words were "cash flow." As a teen he passionately pursued a music career as a drummer with a band that aimed to create technically complex rock inspired by the likes of Wishbone Ash, Deep Purple, and Led Zeppelin.

Playing and touring exposed Alan to the business side of music, and when his band, though talented and well-received, was unable to secure a recording contract, Alan spotted an opportunity to move into the professional audio industry. This led to decades of buying, scaling up, selling, and merging businesses, as well as successfully bouncing back from his share of losses and missteps. His business, Turbosound, one of the leading professional audio manufacturers used by the world's major bands and music venues, won Britain's Queen's Award for Export in 1987.

Over time, Alan began answering calls from colleagues, and friends of colleagues, seeking business advice. He found he deeply enjoyed helping others, and in time he pursued training and experience in coaching and mediation.

Before his stroke, Alan divided his time between London and Forest Row, a rural village to the south surrounded by countryside, where he lived with his wife, Ruth, a former dancer, Feldenkrais practitioner, and yoga instructor.

Alan hails from a family that afforded him wealth, connections, and opportunities not available to most people. "Privilege and entitlement, yes. I was born and brought up in a family with a sense of that, then I went into the British private school system, the equivalent of Phillips Exeter Academy, and it reinforced that sense of privilege and entitlement."

During his darkest days in the hospital he realized he wanted to help as many business people as he could, but that meant expanding his business, and he was afraid to do it. To him, expanding his business meant trying to attract more demographically diverse clients. And that would require a move out of his comfort zone.

"There's an arrogance with being a 'best kept secret,'" he revealed, "and 'I only do business with friends of friends of friends I'm introduced to personally.' There is a piece of that that's arrogant, that I'm above the fray, I don't sell, I don't advertise, everything is easy."

He was not only afraid he would be out of his comfort zone with a new type of client, but to reach them he would also have to engage in new (to him) types of business practices: marketing and advertising.

"I had to get through the fear of being recorded, of being videoed, and even having a web site—oh, my God, what colors do I have to have?—and taking years, you know, not making up my mind, procrastinating."

"I made myself a promise that if I got out of there alive, I would stop being so bloody fearful. I would go wider. I would go for it." Being pushed to make this decision, said Alan, was one of the deepest, most profound effects of his stroke.

Before he could even turn towards transforming his existing business, though, up cropped some other fears.

After the stroke, Alan kept working with clients right from his hospital room, but only on the phone because he didn't want them to see his stroke-affected right side. "Alan was fearful that if his clients found out he'd had a stroke," Ruth remembered, "they would not want to work with him. That was a big thing for him."

Work was Alan's "anchor," Ruth said, and so she supported him in that. "He was having to use his left hand on his laptop, so I would type stuff for him." In those early days, she was in shock. "It wasn't clear what was going on. He'd been diagnosed with MS at first." At times Ruth felt incredulous, but she just kept putting one foot in front of the other. "OK," she remembered thinking while helping him shower, "this is the next thing that's presenting itself."

Alan said he couldn't have recovered so well without Ruth's support, which she described as "holding space" for Alan. But she did an enormous amount on the practical level, too. She accompanied him to therapy sessions in the hospital, and once he was home, she continued to help him with both work and therapy there.

That could only last so long, though. "I thought I could do it all," she recalled. Over time, she realized she had to put her self care front and center.

"I had to be very, very clear about my rhythm. It's not like having a little child, but you are living around the rhythm of another because you are supporting them in their basic needs and you have to give up your own." Insomnia, she recalled, was a problem initially because of not knowing what the next day would bring.

Ruth took care of herself in part by taking refuge in small day-to-day rituals. "Sorting out the kitchen and emptying the dishwasher become like anchors for me." More important was moving and breathing, which she did through yoga and Feldenkrais (a system of mindful movement that helps stimulate the brain to forge new neural pathways), walking, hiking, and spending time in the garden. "You learn what it is you need, it wasn't a given," she said.

***

"Vasculitis is an autoimmune disease," said Alan, "and in hindsight, I'd been suffering from it for 10 years without knowing it. It gave me weird sensations starting in 2005 until my stroke. Tingling, numbness, electric shocks. I'd had tests and was told I had neuritis. And then it went bang!"

Alan credits a host of activities that he believes helped him make progress in recovery.

He forced himself to be "active, active, active," in both mind and body, even though it was difficult. He did standard physical therapy, but he also walked, swam, and used a TENS machine (low-voltage transcutaneous electrical nerve stimulation to help relieve pain).

He believes the fact that he never stopped working, even in the hospital, was beneficial. "It was probably what got me in the hospital in the first place," he reflected, "but it kept my brain active."

Ruth's ongoing study of somatic approaches to support her own wellness had led her to Feldenkrais. At around three months post-stroke, Ruth suggested he try it. "I tried it. If someone said, 'try red socks,' I'd try it," he joked, adding, "I found it helpful, it played a big part in my recovery."

Ruth started to train as a Feldenkrais practitioner just after Alan had his stroke. "It was very fascinating with everything that Alan was facing, and it drove my study and learning of the method."

The method was different from traditional therapies in that in the first few sessions it focused on Alan's left side, rather than his stroke-affected right. "Of course [other therapists] had been focusing on his right side, but that just made Alan focus on what he couldn't do, or do as well as he liked. But in the first [Feldenkrais] session, he felt a difference with how he stood up and in his sense of stability."

With Feldenkrais, Ruth said, it's not necessarily about regaining past function, but about relearning how to move. "In relearning, you might actually be able to do things better," she said. Ruth noted that this approach helps preserve a person's dignity. "It brought a slightly interesting reframe which was full of possibility, and that was emotionally really helpful to Alan."

Though Ruth had both a personal and professional interest in Feldenkrais, she knew she had to step back from Alan's process. "Alan might make very different choices than I would. Within this journey he needs to lead and it's not about me saying, well, you should do [this or that.] I learned to just be his partner, not one of his therapists. This was a big learning for me."

*****

"This was very helpful," Alan said, pointing to a drum kit set up in a corner of their light-filled home in Forest Row. He picked up the sticks again after his stroke, but this time, for rehab.

"Drums were a big chunk," he said. "I couldn't grip the stick to begin with. The right foot is the driver of the band, it's the kick pedal, the bass drum, the boom boom boom, and I couldn't make it work because I had drop foot. That was very frustrating." Alan learned a new strategy: to pick up his knee to drop his whole foot down. Many drummers, stroke or no, play this way.

"The right hand is for the hi-hat and cymbals," he explained, "and to this day I can't do it fast. It was quite upsetting and depressing, but I knew that it was good for the recovery." At least he could hit the snare drum, he said. "So I could play left hand and left foot as well as ever, and horribly on the right, but gradually the right improved, so it was a mixed feeling. It wasn't fun, wasn't fun, no, no. It's kind of recovery and rehab with music, and it wasn't fun. It was recovery and I knew I had to do it."

Alan's electronic drum kit allows him to put headphones on and play along with recordings.

Often, he would play along with "Free," one of his favorite bands. "The drummer is a hero of mine, Simon Kirke. He's a top English blues and rock drummer who went on to play in Bad Company. He brings everything down to a minimum. I love listening to Free, and thank goodness Simon Kirke's right hand and right foot are often half-beats, they are slow, and that was something I could play to."

The drums, he said, not only help with neuroplasticity, they are great to hit cathartically, too.

"My doctor says there is no doubt in his mind that the Feldenkrais and the drumming helped. Considering the severity of the stroke, I've made a great recovery."

***

Alan's number one piece of advice for other stroke survivors is to get professional help for the emotional and psychological challenges that stroke can cause, such as the frustration, anger, and sadness that he experienced.

"It doesn't matter what technique they use, it's whatever works for you. Find somebody where there is trust and chemistry, who you can say anything to, and you won't be judged. Spend the money. It's crucial. Other things will come as a result of getting that sorted."

Beyond that, he recommends people read *Man's Search for Meaning* by Victor Frankl. "In other words, have a purpose," he counsels. "There's got to be something to look forward to, something to aim for at the worst possible time. It can be a very hard thing to invent, so it's got to come from the heart. Having a purpose is a massive part of this. Mine was to bring my learnings and experience to thousands of people."

He also advises others to not compare themselves with anyone who is further along than them. "Compare yourself with yesterday only. Going from a wheelchair to crutches is a step. It's not, 'oh dear, I've got crutches, look at all the people running around,' it's 'yesterday I was in a wheelchair and today I've made progress.'"

Leaning into one's family and friends for emotional and physical support is another practice he recommends. "You cannot do any of this alone, it's too serious," he said, adding that it's helpful to be with other stroke survivors, too. "Comparing notes and experiences with them is crucial."

Ruth's advice for loved ones of stroke survivors who want to care for them is "build around yourself a good tribe of support." She recounted how blessed she felt to have an "extraordinary family," made up of her father, friends, and her children who were at home at the time.

She said family caregivers often confidently say, "oh, I can do all of this. And maybe you can at the beginning, but partners or loved ones have to have their own support. It's about sustainability."

"Through this journey," reflected Ruth, "Alan has both met his biggest fears and had the privilege of understanding that most of them are not going to come true." When he told his clients—five months post-stroke—that he'd had a stroke, "nobody stopped working with him," she said with a smile.

***

"This journey is something no one would have wished for," she said. "He loves hiking and to be active, but he has a lot of residual neurological pain and issues with balance, so there are some things that he can't do currently for very long, but there are so many other gifts that have come from this, extremely amazing gifts."

"Everything you take as a given is not a given anymore," she emphasized, "and that is very, very scary. There does need to be an element of deconstruction, or a slight crumbling of yourself as you know yourself," but, she said, eventually something else comes forward.

In Alan's case, he realized what is truly important. "He wakes up to that time and time again. I'm not suggesting that we all became amazing spiritual beings, just that there were gifts in it."

"Today he is doing work that is more meaningful and fulfilling in some ways. He is now working with clients he may never have worked with before. He is very, very lucky to have been able to carry on and live his life in a way that is meaningful to him. Even people who are very compromised, there is still is meaning in their lives."

***

Alan also said that the stroke helped him accept the fact that he is human. "I am not better than, my body can screw up. Thinking 'I never get ill,' that whole arrogant bollocks, all went out the window."

After he gained a measure of acceptance of his mortality, he gradually learned the lesson that helped him face his fears and take his business to the next level. "There is no one else other than me responsible for everything that's happening to me," he revealed. Alan can now share this learning in an authentic way to his clients today, and it has made his coaching deeper, richer, and more effective.

"So the biggest change was that one: I'm responsible for me and if anybody is going to do anything special in whatever the rest of my life is—and my father died very young—it's got to be me. I've got to get out there and do it. That's what it's given me, the stroke experience. It's been life changing."

CLIMBING THE MOUNTAIN

Lawnae Hunter

by Diane Huie Balay

"Life throws you some tough stuff, but it's how you react that counts. I want to model for my grandchildren that you can get through anything."

Two weeks before Christmas in 2014, Lawnae Hunter stood on top of the bright blue waterslide that her nine-year-old granddaughter Lauren had just slipped down with a squeal and a giggle. Three stories below, Lawnae could see the palm trees, pools, and vacationing families at the Beaches Resort on the Caribbean island of Turks and Caicos.

A few minutes earlier, Lawnae was with her son Danny Hunter and Lauren at the resort pool when Lauren said, "I think I'll go on the waterslide. Want to come with me, Nana?"

"I wanted to be a cool Nana so, of course, I went," Lawnae recalled.

So, Lawnae sat down in the flowing stream of water at the entrance of the slide and pushed off into the tube.

"What I didn't know is the moment I sat down on that slide, life as I knew it was about to end. With each bump from the connecting tubes on the slide, the water seemed to become more ferocious. It was like moving from a flowing stream into a stormy surf within seconds. I thought I was surely drowning. This memory haunts me. It fuels my anxiety and makes it nearly impossible to breathe."

When she splashed into the pool from the tube, Danny rushed to help her out of the water. He knew immediately that something was wrong. "She was choking and the left side of her face had collapsed." He yelled for help and the resort security brought a wheelchair and called an ambulance to take her to the hospital.

Lawnae could still move her left side, and she refused to ride in the ambulance, saying, "Oh, I'm fine. I'm fine." After she changed clothes with Danny's wife Kim's assistance, a resort manager drove them to the hospital.

Even when hospital staff put her on a gurney to wheel her in the hospital, Lawnae didn't realize how serious it was.

"What do you think it is?" she asked, still able to talk.

"We think you had a stroke."

"No. I don't think I had a stroke," Lawnae told them. "Don't call anyone. I don't want to worry anyone." At the time, I prayed and prayed, "Dear Holy Father, heal me and give me strength to be a servant leader and to serve those in my life."

Kim called Lawnae's daughter Lisa Wilber, who like Lawnae, lives in Bend, OR. The Hunters had learned that the Turks and Caicos hospital does not treat strokes. She had to go by air ambulance to Ft. Lauderdale. Lisa scrambled to schedule an air ambulance, but the aircraft was not allowed to leave Miami until the payment cleared. In the meantime, Lawnae's condition was deteriorating. Today, she knows the importance of having ambulance insurance in place.

Kim flew with Lawnae to Florida and went with her to the hospital in Hollywood, a town near Ft. Lauderdale. By the time they reached the hospital, twelve hours had elapsed since her stroke.

When the hospital staff tried to give Lawnae an MRI the next day, Lawnae's condition had deteriorated to the point that it became necessary to intubate her and render her unconscious with drugs. The doctors discovered that she had a large, benign brain tumor that had been there for years that she was unaware of. They believed that pressure from the growing tumor had caused the stroke.

Lawnae was in and out of consciousness in the ICU, trying to rip everything out when she was under. Her younger brother, Patrick Williams, did everything he could to be there. While flying in from Columbia, he found himself spending the night with his cab driver in between travels, sparking a lifelong friendship between them. The moment he arrived he never left her side, especially at night. Lisa flew in from the West Coast to be with her, as did Lawnae's other daughter, Christin Hunter, and Lawnae's friend Ron Salter.

Unable to talk because of the ventilator attached to her trachea, Lawnae used notepads to make her wishes known. "Plane. Fly. Fly." "Gun show. Go get me a gun."

She heard doctors talking across her ICU bed about the swelling in her brain and if it continued, surgery, which she might not survive, would be necessary.

Afraid that she was going to die, Lawnae just wanted to get out of that hospital. From the window beside her bed, she could see a box-shaped robot roaming the hall. The robot delivered medications to the nurses.

"I was absolutely convinced," Lawnae said later, "that if I could flop over on that box, I could ride on it to the front door of the hospital and get a taxi to drive me to Bend, Oregon."

Lawnae wasn't the only one worried that she might die. All of her immediate family were worried, as were all of her employees in her string of real estate-related businesses on the California Central Coast and in Oregon.

Not wanting to panic her business associates, with whom she was very close, Lawnae instructed that they be told nothing except that she had a stroke, was in the hospital, and doing well. They were worried anyway. They were accustomed to a very hands-on, decision-making owner from whom they were hearing nothing.

Lawnae was not always a business owner.

"We were as poor as dirt," Lawnae said. Raised by a single mom in Aptos, CA, who had no assets, she and her brother Patrick took care of each other. When she was fourteen-years-old, Lawnae went to work in a restaurant in the Bay View Hotel to help pay the family bills.

"All the way through high school," Lawnae said, "I would walk down the railroad track after school to go to work."

Pregnant and married at 17, then divorced, Lawnae graduated from high school with baby Lisa to support. College was out of the question, but Lawnae still wanted to find a path to success.

Pouring coffee in the Bay View Hotel coffee shop, Lawnae listened to the conversations between men who were doing very well in real estate.

"I thought, if those 'old codgers' can make money selling real estate, I sure can," she remembered, laughing.

So she started climbing that mountain. At 19, she went to real estate school on the $67.50 her mother borrowed with her first Mastercard. At 21, she got her broker's license; at 22, opened her first real estate office in Santa Cruz, CA; at 24, married an Air Force officer with two children; at 28, owned a real estate company and was raising four kids. In 2003, she sold her extensive real estate business to an affiliate of Warren Buffett's Berkshire Hathaway.

While she lay in the Florida hospital's ICU after her stroke, Lawnae was frightened by hallucinations of horrific spiders on the walls, and weary strangers haunting the hallways. She was also plagued with severe breathing problems due to damage to her trachea when she was intubated.

"If I can just get home to the west coast, I'll be OK," she thought. "I would move mountains to get to Stanford," she added, referring to the renowned hospital in the California academic medical complex associated with Stanford University.

After some serious mountain moving, on New Year's Day 2015, Lawnae winged her way by air ambulance across the country to San Jose, CA, then to Stanford Hospital where she was once again in ICU.

"I remember looking at the clock," she said, "and I couldn't tell time. That was one of the most frightening times in my recovery. At that moment, I questioned if I can't even tell time, then who am I to be? How could I cope in the world I once knew? When children can't tell time, there is a promise that they will learn, but was there even that promise for me?"

Two weeks later, she was moved to Santa Clara Valley Medical Rehabilitation Hospital, a place with staff who refused to see her as anything short of who she was, a human being. Lying on a gurney in the ambulance, unable to move the left side of her body, Lawnae wondered if her life was over. "If I can't move like I always have, then what's the purpose?"

"There I was, petrified. I was riding in an ambulance on a gurney, just one more step towards the uncertainty of who I was to be. In the midst of that confusion appeared a nurse, George, who was like an angel flying into my life. He put his hand on my arm and said, 'We are going to take care of you. You're going to be OK.' Right there, in that moment, I felt at peace for the first time in what seemed like a lifetime."

"I'll love that man as long as I live."

Lawnae's therapy was start and stop, she said, because of her breathing difficulties, and she repeatedly had to return to Stanford Hospital.

"When I left the facility in April, I was still in a wheelchair and I was just beginning to walk," she recalled, singing the praises of the staff there. "I was in the parallel bars, holding on. I slowly moved my right foot forward, then my left foot and a light went on. Oh my gosh, I'm walking! My whole body flooded with happiness and I squealed with joy. I'm going to be able to walk!"

Lawnae continued her journey as an outpatient of a rehab facility in Santa Cruz, climbing the formidable mountain that would lead to a different but very interesting and very fulfilling life. It was, and is, a hard journey filled with physical and emotional struggles and plagued with setbacks. She had more surgeries on her damaged trachea. Sometimes she would fall and the fire department would have to come pick her up. One particularly bad fall in her third year post-stroke resulted in a concussion and a broken arm and put her back in the hospital for a month, placing her in the promising hands of Bend's St. Charles Rehabilitation group.

Lawnae used that time to reflect and meet new people in the stroke community. She became passionate about cheering on stroke survivors through recovery, and dedicated her life to the people on this journey.

"Our world is therapy," she said. "You have to go beyond the work you do with your therapist and work constantly at home." Throughout her recovery, Lawnae pursued a number of alternative therapies as well as the usual occupational and physical therapy programs. She participated in a Stanford stem cell research program. She particularly appreciates Feldenkrais therapy, which made her aware of crucial brain and body connections.

When asked what motivated her to work so hard in therapy, Lawnae replied, "I had to show my three grandchildren that life throws you some tough stuff, but it's how you react that counts. I wanted to model for them that you can get through anything. You just have to work hard and be smart every moment you can"

Little by little, Lawnae's abilities increased. She could get out of a chair, stand up straight, and walk around the island in her kitchen as long as she held on. It was extremely difficult and took enormous effort, but she could do it.

"My biggest fear was going to a public bathroom," she said. "I'm so social I wanted to go to restaurants, shopping, to the grocery store." She was afraid she would not be able to do those things again. Finally, she was able to do the very difficult task of using a public bathroom. "There I was, sitting on the toilet and crying for joy because I had climbed that mountain."

On her sixty-sixth birthday, Lawnae was staying at her vacation home in Aptos and was determined to be standing at the door—a huge achievement—when a group of old friends from the California Central Coast arrived to help her celebrate. And to their great delight, she did it. The four women, all of them retired, are special friends whom Lawnae calls her "Cronies." Although living in different states, the five women enjoyed laughing, cooking, eating out, going to the theater, traveling, and just hanging out together whenever they could. So when the Cronies got out of the car wearing glittering black top hats and ready to perform the birthday song, Lawnae was already laughing.

With the Cronies at her side, Lawnae did a series of firsts like visiting her favorite bakery, dining at a favorite restaurant, even attending the theater.

"With the Cronies, my life was returning to normal," she said. "We did so much creative and silly stuff together. It was very healing."

Depression can, and usually does, plague stroke survivors and Lawnae was no exception. By her third year post-stroke, Lawnae had to deal with a pretty severe bout of it. Although through therapy she was making slow but remarkable improvement with her left leg, her left arm, whom she named Betty, remained paralyzed no matter how hard Lawnae worked. She had even promised Betty a diamond bracelet if she would "wake up." But Betty refused to wake up.

"I just had to come to grips with that. Finally, I said to myself, 'Lawnae, you can still have a great life even without the use of your left arm.' And with that acceptance, my whole life got a lot easier."

Another emotion Lawnae struggled with was shame. She blamed herself for her stroke and the pain and collateral damage it caused her family. She beat herself up about it for a long time. The reason? About 30 days before the stroke, Lawnae had a TIA, a small stroke, on the way to an ophthalmologist appointment. She suddenly could not speak. After a while, she was able to speak again and she continued on to her appointment and never mentioned it to the doctor.

"Had I told the doctor or gone to the emergency room then," she said, "they would have discovered the tumor." She is convinced that treatment then would have prevented the massive stroke later. That is why, she emphasizes, it is so important for people to learn the signs of stroke and to lose no time in going to the emergency room. Lives can be saved. Brain damage can be prevented.

Family members also can suffer misplaced guilt and shame. Years after the stroke, Lawnae's son Danny broke down in tears. "I will forever feel that the reason she had the stroke is because I encouraged her to go on that slide. What was I thinking?"

Strokes are not without their blessings, and Lawnae counts hers every night with the support of her Christian faith giving her a strong foundation to lean on. They include the love and support of her friends and family, and her brother Patrick who has been by her side every step of the way. Among her greatest blessings, she said, is that her two daughters, who are half-sisters born 10 years apart and who are as different as daylight and dark, have become very close. Lisa and Christin agree that they communicate with each other far more often and have banded together to watch after and care for their mother. Today, they are the dynamic trio.

It worries her daughters that Lawnae continues to work so hard at her businesses and other projects.

"She is doing way too much," said Christin. "But her tenaciousness and determination are what saved her life. I am beyond grateful that she has those attributes. Otherwise, she would not have been able to withstand all that she went through."

Lawnae learned everything she possibly could about strokes and stroke recovery. This led her to a conference of experts in 2016 where she met Dr. Steven Goins, a neurologist in Bend. Dr. Goins shared her passion for helping stroke survivors and educating the public about stroke awareness. Using his medical knowledge and her business skills and her years of working with nonprofit organizations, they started what would become Stroke Awareness Oregon, the publishers of this book.

Lawnae's passion for aiding stroke survivors and for educating the public about the signs and symptoms is channeled through this life saving, nonprofit organization. Stroke Awareness Oregon achieves these goals through support groups, monthly lectures, online materials and resources, social activities, and more. For more information about the organization, go to strokeawarenessoregon.org.

To her fellow stroke survivors, Lawnae says: "Don't be afraid. Be strong. You can do this! Don't ever give in to the fear. Fear is our enemy!"

Snow Geese

Thousands of snow geese
take to the sky
out of Yosemite.
Grey black grasses below.

White birds with
Tips of black
Heading to the Arctic,
Red beaks,
Cawing hums,
Flying above
bare branches
into a pale blue sky.

Sudden distance now,
Small red V's against
The igloo white sun,
Flying now
Into the clouds . . .

Sun over mountain edge
Turns waterfall golden
To red.
Fiery, burning.
Molten water,
Cascading.

by Monza Naff ©2017

THE THREE MIRACLES

Michael Erwin

by Kerry Chaput

"I needed to understand that this was a brain injury, not a body injury. It heals on a different timeline."

Hard work and motivation.

That's what got you where you wanted to be, according to Michael Erwin of Raleigh, NC. It was true for him, a Senior Vice President of Merchandise with a forty-two-year career in the retail industry. So in 2016, when Michael's world was turned upside down by the unexpected loss of the career he'd devoted his life to, he knew how to motivate himself and work hard to get on his feet again.

A year later, he and his wife Jennifer had no idea that Michael would once again have to rely on these inner resources to face the greatest challenge of their lives.

On a September morning in 2017, Michael and Jennifer were having a playful argument about who would get out of the bed first. Michael lost, so he sat up, intending to hop in the shower. He started to sway back and forth and when Jennifer realized he was also slurring his speech, she knew instantly he was having a stroke.

The paramedics arrived right away. In the emergency room of the stroke center at UNC REX Hospital in Raleigh, they learned Michael had suffered a hemorrhage in the cerebellum, a type of stroke for which there are usually grim outcomes.

Jennifer's mother Pam recalled rushing to the hospital, not knowing what had happened. She walked up to the hospital doors to find Jennifer and Michael's thirty-three-year-old son Chase with tears rolling down his cheeks. Jennifer told her mother, "Mama, it's really bad."

In the hospital Jennifer remembered the doctors and nurses speaking over Michael. She stopped and asked them to speak to him. "I could tell he was in there. He wasn't speaking, but he was still communicating to me." Michael had aphasia at the time and although he knew what he wanted to say, he couldn't find the words.

"This was my first miracle," Michael said. "I lived."

"I can't explain it, but it didn't even cross my mind that I wouldn't live," he said. Michael spent five weeks in the hospital, first in the ICU, and then in Duke Regional Inpatient Rehabilitation Center in Durham. "My grandson Coven had just turned one, and it was amazing that he knew I was hurt. He would pat me gently on my foot, trying to help me feel better."

"I was so tired," recalled Michael. "I just wanted to sleep. Speech therapy in the hospital was just awful. How could I not know the simplest of phrases? I hadn't yet understood that my brain was injured."

During his time in the hospital, Jennifer didn't leave Michael's side. He couldn't communicate his needs, but Jennifer was always able to decipher them. She felt they had a deep connection that transcended words. Michael says his wife was so in tune with him, she would often finish his sentences. "Getting her to stop when I got better was very difficult!" he joked.

Toward the end of his hospital stay, Michael experienced his second miracle.

His blood pressure was spiking, and they couldn't get it under control. "I've had high blood pressure since I was thirty-five. I thought it was under control. I didn't know how dangerous it was." With a recent bleed in his brain, the high blood pressure was extremely dangerous. Luckily, the hospital had a blood pressure specialist who was able to diagnose the problem right away. He swooped in, adjusted Michael's medication, and saved him at a crucial moment. His blood pressure has been normal ever since.

It was a long, difficult six months. "He was really hard on himself," Jennifer recalled. "He had spent his career motivating others and helping them, and when it came to himself, he was finding it very difficult." Michael had been through several leg surgeries in the years prior to the stroke and he was frustrated that this was so different. "I kept thinking all I had to do was work hard. I needed to understand that this was a brain injury, not a body injury. It heals on a different timeline."

Speech was his most frustrating task. "I could recall really complicated words but not the most basic ones." Jennifer said she had to look words up occasionally to understand his meaning. His home speech therapist assigned a list of 100 synonyms and 100 antonyms for Michael to practice. He stuck to his therapy and worked on every single word on the list.

"I hated those exercises." No matter how frustrated he was, he didn't stop trying. "My voice was still very weak. You know what brought the strength back? Bantering with my father-in-law every night while watching *Wheel of Fortune*. It was a lot of fun-spirited aggravation."

During his recovery, Michael and Jennifer moved in with her parents in Oxford, about 50 miles north of their home. Out in the rural farm country, Michael had the support he needed to work on rehab and Jennifer could still work to maintain their insurance. "My in-laws are wonderful people. Pam helped me work through my exercises, helped me transfer and move, and cooked wonderful meals for us."

"I prayed for Jennifer's needs as much as Michael's," Pam said. "Michael is the bravest man I know. He fought a long battle every day. And my brave daughter fought along with him." They all grew closer as a family, calling on friends, extended family, and faith to get them through. "Michael became the son I never had."

***

After a course of rehab, Michael graduated to outpatient physical therapy. "I was in a really busy clinic and I felt they kept telling me what I couldn't do. They told me the first day that I might not walk again. I looked at them and said, "If you think I'm not going to walk again, you've got the wrong person."

They both agreed he wasn't going to get the care he needed at that clinic, so Jennifer set out to interview different facilities. They decided on Steps for Recovery in nearby Cary, NC. Michael started twice a week. On his first visit, his new therapist said, "I want to see you walk around this building." He knew he had found the right fit.

"So much of recovery is finding health-care professionals that get you and your personality," Jennifer said. "People need to understand that if someone isn't working for you, it's important to find the one who will." Michael and Jennifer continue to dictate how his recovery will go and they won't let people tell them what he can't do.

Jennifer admitted that Michael's stroke was devastating to her. "I would put on a brave face for him and our Chase. They didn't know I was crying in the shower where they couldn't see me." She feels it was the tiny moments of progress that gave her hope. "When he would have a breakthrough, it was like a reminder that we were going to get through this."

She tells stroke survivors that their support system will change. "It might not be who you thought it would be, but people step up and want to help. I had to learn to let them," she said.

***

And the third miracle? Michael experienced it about eight months post-stroke. He'd had an ongoing, burning question about what his life would look like now. What was his purpose?

"I had a vivid dream one night that I opened a nonprofit organization to help stroke survivors. After I had that same dream three times, I made a promise to God. If I could walk around the rehab building by January, I agreed to start a nonprofit."

It was no surprise that Michael did walk around the building by January. One-third of a mile without his cane. And not only that, that month he was also strong enough to move with Jennifer back into their home in Raleigh. His therapist wanted to graduate him, and he grew emotional. "I had gotten attached. I didn't want to move on. It felt like giving up."

He has since learned that with a stroke, you can't look back. "My therapist gave me my independence again. It might look different, but my life was full again. I could drive and spend time with friends. Have a life again." He knew progress was always possible if he believed in himself. In January of 2019, Michael began to walk completely without a cane.

And he kept his promise. In 2019, he and Jennifer started their non-profit "Believe Stroke Recovery Foundation." Its aim is simple: to help survivors afford the long course of recovery after their stroke. Insurance only covers so much, but as Michael has learned, progress continues as long as you keep working towards it.

"We want to put the spotlight on recovery," Jennifer said. "Change people's thinking and talk about the challenges stroke survivors and their families go through."

Michael thinks he has changed since his stroke three and a half years ago. "I used to be high-strung. I'm changed. I let go of grudges. Now I see the importance of seeing the good."

Jennifer is happy to see he no longer hides his silly, playful side from people. "He's less guarded. More carefree. Everything we've gone through has made our marriage stronger."

As he reflected on his journey, he said, "no one really knows what the journey after stroke looks like. I have yet to meet a stroke survivor who ever thought they were at risk for one. That includes me."

Three main principles continue to guide him: faith, perspective, and patience. "I often close my eyes and thank God for giving me a second chance."

EMERGING
FROM THE SMOKE

Orlena Shek

by Amy Doherty

"Wash away the heaviness that lines
The contours of your soul
Until it's as light as an alabaster sunset.
Forest fires may burn amid a pandemic.
During times like this,
You fight to rewrite each story into a triumph."

–Orlena Shek (from the forthcoming poetry anthology *Emerging
from the Smoke: A Collection of Warrior Voices*)

"How do you get through a day? How do you live with the disabilities that you have?"

Orlena Shek looked at the faces of students attending her Zoom talk for her alma mater, Castilleja School, an all-girls school in Palo Alto, CA. The year was 2020 and Orlena was nearly a decade into recovery from a severe stroke she had at age thirty-three.

"In your life," she told the girls, "unexpected things are going to come up and you may be physically incapacitated, but you need to be mentally strong. My philosophy is "Mind over Matter," so I strengthen my mind to use it to overcome any physical limitations I may have."

In 2011, Orlena was an extraordinarily talented open source lawyer for a tech company based in Sunnyvale. Attorney Anne Hoge, a former colleague, wrote that Orlena was "highly respected by her clients and peers, someone with a brilliant legal mind, an ability to make things happen, and a way of inspiring those around her."

On December 29, Orlena was working from home and decided to take her twenty-one-month-old daughter on an errand during her lunch break. As Orlena was driving on Route 92, her vision blurred and a headache grew. She realized she needed to get off the freeway to safety, at which point she lost control of her car and crashed into the center divider of the highway.

While both mother and daughter survived the accident, Orlena's headache became unbearable. Her nanny came and picked up her daughter. Her siblings, in town for the holidays, picked Orlena up and took her home. When Orlena got home, her head was still killing her, so she called 911 herself. Then she collapsed.

Orlena had experienced a massive hemorrhagic stroke on the right side, one that less than 30 percent of people survive.

Fortunately, the on-call doctor in the ER had worked with Dr. Gary Steinberg, a world-renowned expert on "moyamoya" disease at Stanford Hospital. He suspected moyamoya and to stabilize Orlena and keep her alive, he transferred her to Stanford where she was put into a medically-induced coma for almost a month. She was then officially diagnosed with moyamoya.

In Japanese, moyamoya means "a puff of smoke." Patients with moyamoya have an abnormal vascular network located in the base of the brain. When Dr. Steinberg and the Stanford team felt Orlena was stable enough from the stroke, they performed two successful brain surgeries. Team Orlena quickly formed. It consisted of her dedicated husband, her parents, daughter, and her siblings and in-laws. She was nearly six months in the hospital recovering and then she went home around Mother's Day in 2012. Then began her 10-year rehabilitation.

Though her work had been a big part of her identity, she left her career to focus on her rehab and her family. Her team continued to support her during her recovery, but she also exercised that mental strength she told the students at Castilleja about. She credits her parents and grandparents with instilling that strength and resilience in her. She recalled their unwavering capacity to see the positive and to overcome hardship. "My mother always saw the world through her perpetual sunny outlook," she said. Orlena's optimism, her doctors will attest, helped her save her own life.

Anne remembered the aftermath of Orlena's stroke. "I had the sorrow of watching her battle through extensive hospitalization and rehabilitation, and move away from her legal career." But through it all, she said, Orlena has risen "with her characteristic joy, strength, and spirit."

In 2017, tragedy struck again: Orlena's beloved mother died, leaving Orlena and her family grieving. Out of this devastating loss, Orlena's son was born exactly nine months later.

Orlena eventually followed her intuition to sign up for a creative writing class at a local community college. She found that writing was a salve to her bereavement over the loss of her mother. Though she had never been to therapy, it was therapeutic to write her words out on paper, and it helped her heal. It helped her heal so much that poetry became a major part of her recovery.

She joined a Facebook support group started by Tara MacInnes, also a patient of Dr. Steinberg's, and a long-time moyamoya advocate who launched a movement to bring awareness to the rare disease via World Moyamoya Day. When the pandemic shut the world down in March 2020, the moyamoya survivors began to share their poetry in their Facebook group.

Orlena was drawn to their writing, what she calls "Warrior Poetry," and as she began to write some of her own, an idea emerged in her mind: to collect the poetry and publish it in one volume. If she gleaned so much from these words of perseverance and hope, others would, too. More, this would be a way she could honor her parents on a level that felt fitting to the monumental role they had played in her life.

This past October, Orlena lost her father, who had always provided her constant love and support. "He was so gregarious and charming and I spoke to him almost every day." From her grief, Orlena again connected with her need to honor her parents' positive influence on her life.

She continued compiling original poems and haiku from her fellow warrior-survivors, a project that she now saw as a love letter to her parents. An excerpt from her poem, "When Night Descends," reads:

"Don't be afraid if it shrouds the truth that was meant to set you free. Dance into the darkness with your partner, to keep time with hope

Because when morning breaks amid the stillness of your faith - We will carry on."

In photos and words, the end of the collection provides some history of Orlena's parents and grandparents that not only honors them, but also shows how they passed along the wisdom and strength that have held her up and kept her going.

Set to be published in 2021 by Archway Publishing from Simon & Schuster, *Emerging from the Smoke: A Collection of Warrior Voices* is the fruit of Orlena's collaboration with 20 other warrior-survivors of various conditions like stroke or moyamoya. Offering words of comfort for current and future survivors, the book showcases what it's like to "emerge from the smoke" of stroke or other health challenges and what people can learn from listening to these survivors. It also provides a resource of information for stroke or brain injury survivors and their families.

"Unanticipated attacks on one's health can leave a person isolated, resentful, and self-absorbed," wrote Elyce Melmon, a poet and playwright in the Bay Area. Instead, she said, Orlena proves the opposite with the book. She shows that "camaraderie, optimism, and selflessness can be healing and rewarding."

Orlena is excited about the cover art which is based on a scan of a moyamoya brain as a "puff of smoke" with artistic renderings of various stroke warriors "emerging" from or superimposed on that scan. One of the sketches is clearly Orlena herself striding confidently out of the smoke. The blue in the background, she pointed out, is official "moyamoya blue."

The project, Orlena said, was about "taking something bad and making something good from it."

Orlena acknowledged the difficulties she faces with a "trifecta" that may be unique to her: being female, disabled, and Asian amid the recent rise in Asian American hate facing her community in 2021. Along with her work advocating for stroke warriors, she volunteers with "Stand For Asians," an activist group in the Bay Area. At the heart of these struggles, though, is hope and her positive attitude, just like her parents modeled for her.

"There's always something profound to be learned from Orlena," said Anne. "For me, how to live with grace, positivity, and fortitude in the face of adversity."

Out of her positive attitude came the decision to share her experiences and use her voice to help others at organizations she cares about, such as Castilleja School, her former employer in Sunnyvale, local stroke organizations, and her former law school, Santa Clara University School of Law. The Pacific Stroke Association (PSA) honored her with an invitation to speak at their Annual Stroke Conference in 2019, and then at their annual gala a month later. She returned to speak at PSA in 2020 and 2021. A percentage of proceeds from *Emerging from the Smoke* will go directly to the Pacific Stroke Association. Orlena plans to expand her speaking engagements—and showcase the book—via her upcoming web site.

"When [Orlena] shared her journey battling this little known disease, I finally had a true appreciation of her strength and tenacity," said former Interim Dean Anna Han, one of Orlena's professors at Santa Clara University School of Law. "Where most people would have given up, Orlena not only conquered this terrible disease, she is promoting awareness and building a community for other sufferers."

In the words of Dr. Steinberg himself, who wrote a beautiful foreword to the book: "This poetry anthology, spearheaded by Orlena, is a testament to her fortitude and determination that serves to inspire us all."

THE SPARK

Gunner Mench

by Ellen Santasiero

"I try a lot of things and if something gives me
a positive response, I stay with it."

Two weeks after two strokes paralyzed Gunner Mench's left side and blinded his right eye, he experienced a pivotal moment.

He was in a rehab facility near his home on the Big Island of Hawai'i. That day a nurse was sending electrical impulses to muscles on Gunner's left forearm. She was using a small device called a neuro-muscular electrical stimulation (NMES) unit. The goal was to make it possible for Gunner to open his fist on his own. She'd done the same thing the day before, but when Gunner tried to open his fist on his own, no dice.

But today he was willing to try again. Just like the day before, the nurse administered 10 impulses; Gunner's fist opened 10 times. She then stopped the impulses and asked Gunner to try to open his fist on his own.

"It took!" he said, recalling the moment. "From then on, I knew I had a chance of recovery."

Before his strokes hit in 2016, Gunner was sixty-two and he and his wife Elli were busy art gallery owners on the Big Island's north side specializing in the work of local artists. They were long-time donors to the preservation of the Kohala watershed. A Porsche enthusiast, Gunner had just been appointed Liaison for the Big Island to the Porsche Club of America's Hawai'i Region. He served on his church board, chaired the local Republican Party and the local traffic safety committee, and he was on the mayor's Hawai'i County Highway Safety Council.

"The strokes," said Gunner, "stopped all that." At least for a while.

Gunner had been athletic and in great shape all his life, running, skiing, and safeguarding others on ski patrol. Growing up in New England he had what he called "a wonderful upbringing" filled with sports and travel as well as beauty and craftsmanship. He taught himself guitar as a youngster, played concerts, and achieved Eagle Scout. His parents let him build a chemistry lab in the basement, and his grandfather gave seven-year-old Gunner an accordion.

His father was an internationally renowned photographer and his mother a master watchmaker. Gunner eventually became a licensed automotive mechanic, and he believes his ability to think in four dimensions—three dimensions plus time, the fourth dimension— came from his parents. That thinking style informs his approach to wellness today.

***

On April 1, 2016, Gunner started feeling spacey while having breakfast at the Hawaiian Style Cafe, a cheery place popular with locals in
Waimea. After he ate, he felt a little better, but when he got home,
he got out of the car, took two steps, and stopped. "I thought, something's not right."

When he grabbed the front doorknob, his fingers were tingling. "I
thought, dammit, I'm having a stroke." Elli called 911. An ambulance
rushed Gunner to North Hawai'i Community Hospital. By the time
they got there, his whole left side was gone. "Zero," he said. Turned
out he had had two strokes. A piece of plaque had split in two, one
lodged in his brainstem, and the other in the visual processing area.
"No right eye and no left side!" he exclaimed.

Fortunately, within two hours of the stroke, a doctor in Oahu was
on a monitor at the foot of Gunner's hospital bed directing staff to
administer tPA, a medicine that dissolves clots. "That minimized the
damage. That's probably why the brainstem stroke didn't kill me."

***

While in ICU for almost a week, Gunner started to move his left leg.
"As soon as I moved it, they made me move it over and over, but that
was about it. And my right eye would not focus."

While physical and occupational therapists continued to work with
his left leg and hand, and a speech therapist helped him restore movement in his facial muscles, Gunner learned, at least in theory, how to
get in and out of a wheelchair, and then a van.

Meanwhile, Elli had to keep running the gallery. "It was a major challenge for her," said Gunner, as they handle more than 200 artists. "We work eight days a week," he reflected.

When he came home he was still bedridden. Elli helped him shower, and he had to use a bed pan. He kept up outpatient rehab back at the hospital, though. At home in bed one day, he was determined to wheel himself to the bathroom, but he fell just trying to sit up by himself and split his ear on the edge of the nightstand. "Another trip to the ER!"

He could eventually get into the wheelchair on his own, and then advanced rapidly to using a walker which helped him gain more stability. He soon traded in the walker for a cane. "I got to the point where I could go 30 to 40 feet down the hallway and back doing squats." At home, he installed grab bars for safety.

After his insurance-sponsored rehab ended, he took his entire rehab plan into his own hands. "I had been an athlete," he said. "I knew what I needed to do."

He discovered that North Hawai'i had what they called an "outpatient club," where community members could use the equipment on their own for a low monthly fee. He liked the resistance machine for the lower body because it could help him continue to rebuild strength and stamina in his left leg. The exercise was arduous, but the incentive for Gunner was strong. "I wanted to be able to drive my classic Porsches again!" At first, Gunner could only clock 20 pushes before taking a break.

Around this time he was delighted to be walking well enough with a cane to visit the Porsche Club Parade event in Vermont and got to test out some tires with Michelin. "On the first drive they gave me a brand new Porsche. My leg still didn't work, but the car was an automatic."

Back in Hawai'i, he hit his workouts hard, and eventually achieved 100 pushes at a time on the resistance machine. "That enabled me to push in a clutch, shift gears, and steer."

***

Some of the hardest moments for Gunner were on days he called "dizzy days." Bad days. Days when he felt he'd taken a step back. But he started to notice a pattern. "Every time I'd have a dizzy day, the next day I would take two steps forward. I'd be less dizzy. I'd be stronger and more capable." He thus learned to celebrate the dizzy days.

Whenever things got hard, he would tap his ability to turn negatives into positives. "If something is wrong, you have to ask, how do I get better? How can I compensate for it?"

Gunner encourages other survivors whenever he has the opportunity. One day a survivor came into the gallery in a wheelchair with a cramped-up arm. "They never tried NMES on him, so I suggested he try it. I love to share my positive experiences and if I can help, that's important."

***

"Everything I've done in life prepared me for this, and nothing prepared me for this," he reflected. But his curious and active mind, his willingness to try everything, and his positive attitude have helped him achieve the best recovery possible.

What works for Gunner is a comprehensive approach, one that reveals that four dimensional thinking style. His physician monitors his health with blood testing. He takes supplements, particularly B vitamins and "super beets." He has an NMES unit to use at home. He sees a neurologist and an acupuncturist. "After acupuncture, I feel like I have springs in my legs." And he reports less brain fog.

"I think acupuncture helps heal the neurological connections to a great extent." All of these thing contribute to his health, he explained. "It all works together."

In 2019, he survived a heart attack while working out at rehab. "My neurologist calls me Lazarus because MRI studies show that my brain has shrunk so severely that I should be a vegetable. He says I have created new pathways in my brain in amazing ways to compensate after the strokes. He credits this recovery to my determination," said Gunner.

Post heart attack, being on blood thinners, he has to be careful to not fall or or cut himself, so while increasing his physical activity, he's had to become more aware of his surroundings. Again, that's hard for him, but his attitude is off the charts. "I've just always been positive," he said. "What is my blood type? B positive," he joked.

When he considered how the stroke experience changed him, he said that while he was a strong Christian before the strokes, the experience enhanced his belief in God. "I have more gratitude," he added, "more joy, and more appreciation for everything I have."

***

Two years after the strokes, Gunner experienced another milestone in his recovery. At that point, he still couldn't feel anything with his left fingers. He was taking his usual shower, and while washing the side of his head with his left hand, he felt sensation in his left fingertips. "I could feel the contour of my ear! That was elation. I was so overjoyed!"

Today, Gunner is back at the gallery, once again working "eight days a week" alongside Elli, and getting involved in the community again. He is now founding president of the 150-member strong Big Island Hawai'i Porsche Club of America, vice chair of the Highway Safety Council, active with the Republican party, and attending church. Remembering his grandfather, he's also picked up the accordion again.

***

Recalling how he opened his left fist by himself only two weeks after his strokes, he said, "If you have that one spark, everything is possible. You know you can try the next thing." He tells survivors to try things regardless of the outcome. "And don't quit after the first attempt. Try again. It's worked for me, it's a fact. I'm a living fact."

He also advises people to get as much help as they can and challenge themselves as much as they can early on. "The sooner you get treatment, the better. Make sure your blood work looks good and you are healthy in other ways. And surround yourself with positive people who don't just cater to you, but also challenge you."

"I don't want anyone to give up hope," he emphasized. "I want people to know that if you make an attempt, if you keep trying, you will find a positive response. You've got to be proactive. Every second of your life you make a decision, so decide to take control. Realize you are the only one responsible for your recovery. When the nurse tried to use the NMES unit on me the second time, I could have said 'don't bother.' I could have decided that, but I didn't. Doing something is better than doing nothing. You've got to make that choice."

"When you've had a stroke, well-meaning people often ask you what percentage are you back to compared to where you were? I'm not sure anyone can make a full recovery, but, of course, they hope to hear you say you are at 100 percent, or even better than before. They are a little taken aback when I answer, 'I'm at 100 percent in my new life, my old one doesn't exist anymore.' A little explanation and they get the fact that, in an instant, stroke changes your life forever, and as survivors, we can be OK with that."

—Ralph Preston

TAKING THE NEXT STEP

Steve Van Houten

by Ellen Santasiero

"If you don't know that you can do it anymore,
you just take the next step …"

It was on the dirt tracks and footpaths of the Camino de Santiago in 2016 that Steve Van Houten learned a lesson that would help him recover from a stroke three years later.

He and his wife Melanie had trained for a year to make the rigorous pilgrimage from St. Jean Pied de Port in France to Santiago de Compostela in Spain. Before the Camino, Steve was strong, in decent shape, and he had trained, but, he said, "it was a hard slog, 13.5 miles a day for 42 days!"

When they were tired and sore and wanted to quit, Steve said that, besides their faith, they learned something practical that helped them through. "If you don't know that you can do it anymore, you just take the next step, and then if you don't know if you can do it anymore, you take the next step. It is simple, but profound. You do what's next. Before you know it you're in León, you're in a new town."

At the time, Steve was somewhat of an expert in the art and science of motivating others. He had been a vocational rehabilitation counselor most of his life, a career he loved, and retired from in 2018. He'd earned a masters in the field, was in private practice for decades, and then spent seven years working with the state of Oregon. He helped people with a wide variety of disabilities find and keep employment. "The hardest part was helping people find their own motivation for working, and then helping them achieve their goals."

Even though he knew what was needed to make progress in recovery, when his stroke hit in 2019, he was challenged to practice what he'd preached to thousands of others for much of his life.

***

About a year after he retired, when he was seventy, Steve woke one October morning with someone's arm draped over his face.

"I asked my wife why her arm was on me and she said it wasn't. I reached up grabbing it and realized it was my own arm, but I couldn't feel it. I told her that and said my leg was numb, too." Melanie, a retired RN, jumped out of bed and asked Steve questions which he later learned were "FAST" questions. "She said she thought I had a stroke and she was calling 911."

"I had lost sensation on the left side of my body, had slurred speech and facial droop, lost my balance so I couldn't walk, and had a field of vision cut." Steve spent a week on a medical floor at St. Charles Medical Center in Bend, OR, and two weeks on the rehab floor.

In the aftermath of his stroke, he remembered his experiences trying to motivate former clients. "What I used to tell them are things I have to remember myself," he said. Now that he is "on the other side with a disability," he thinks of his former clients as mentors, and he's discovered how hard it is to muster the motivation on behalf of his own recovery.

In those two weeks on the rehab floor, he made good progress before coming home with a walker. He then started outpatient physical and occupational therapy at St. Charles, which he said was "fabulous."

Why? The therapists there helped him motivate himself.

"They were absolutely wonderful. They asked me what my main goal was. I said 'to play tennis.'"

***

An avid tennis player since college, Steve said that sport was his main motivation for health and fitness before his stroke. He started when he was eighteen after meeting a girl who invited him to play. "I lost every game to her." He then played for two years for Idaho State on what he called "a lousy team. But that's where I started."

Over the years, he has belonged to five different clubs depending on where he lived.

When he first started rehab, he could barely walk, he couldn't run, and he had trouble keeping his balance. And his left-sided numbness made it so he couldn't tell where he was putting his foot.

"In tennis you run, you watch the ball, you watch the opponent, you try to figure out how you're going to hit the ball. You don't think about your left foot! You know by proprioception where your foot is. Well, I didn't know. It felt impossible to do it."

But his love for tennis, his sense of being a competitor—which means he pushes himself to play very well—was the most motivating force for him.

His physical therapist suggested they take it in steps. "I knew that was right," said Steve. She suggested they break it down into foot movements. "I got a little sensation back in my foot, and I was practicing walking, too, so my sense of my foot was returning. The therapist said I had to wear an ankle brace because the chances of me rolling my ankle were high." She also had him do foot drills.

To help Steve regain function with his arm, she had him work with a student who was doing a practicum as part of his training to become a physical therapist. She gave them pool noodles, took them out in the hallway, and had them sword fight to see who could hit the other one the most.

"She was playing on my competitive spirit!" recalled Steve with delight. "This guy was like twenty-one, he's a kid. I started beating the crap out of him with the pool noodle in my right hand. I was feeling kind of good, and she said, 'good job, Steve. Now do it with your left hand.'

"'That's not fair!' I said. 'I'm right handed!'"

"'I know,' she said. 'Do it with your left hand.'"

While he wasn't as good with his left hand, Steve said he did get in some good shots.

His experience in physical therapy reminded him of his and Melanie's experience on the Camino. After stroke, he said, "the days go by quickly, so you have to take the next step, and let the next day worry about itself."

In time, Steve started playing tennis outdoors with friends, but not as well as he would've liked. One thing he noticed was that his friends were not playing quite as well as they used to. He once asked a friend, "you know I can't run, so why don't you drop shot me? If you do that, you're going to win every point." His friend was going easy on Steve, but Steve wanted to be challenged.

***

When he was a counselor for the state of Oregon, Steve was reminded again and again, that after people find their motivation, they then need to set goals and take concrete steps to reach them.

This concept was driven home to Steve one day by one of his clients.

"This guy was a tribal elder who had a number of disabilities, and I was trying to help him get a job." The man was friendly, but skeptical, and after Steve spoke, the man said, "Well, Mr. Van Houten, I have one question. Tell me the truth, are you blowing smoke up my ass?"

"I burst into laughter," recalled Steve. "I loved that question!"

Steve asked the man what he meant.

"He said, 'I just want to know if the things you are saying are true.'"

"It's important when you are helping people to be positive and encouraging, but if you don't show them concrete ways of getting to their goals, then frankly, it is a bunch of smoke."

He remembers this conversation now when he is doing rehab, and when he is talking with other stroke survivors.

"Habits define who we are as human beings," he explained. "Words are important, but actions show who we are ... Some of us who have survived a stroke may need help setting meaningful goals and practicing habits that will help us reach them."

After setting goals and having concrete steps to reach them, said Steve, people then need to track their progress. "You tend to forget how much progress you've made, or you belittle it because it's not how you used to do things." And, he added, "writing goals and tracking progress keeps you honest with yourself."

***

Even though Steve was motivated by his love for playing tennis, he said he still struggles. "I've found my motivation goes up and down. My attitude is good and not so good. My progress is great and not great. Persistence is required to get through these things. The truth is I've had many difficulties with motivation and I hope understand it more now on a personal level."

He emphasized that hope is a necessary basic ingredient for recovery. "One has to believe they can improve by the goals they set and the work they do."

"My hope begins with my faith in God," he revealed, and then acknowledged that that doesn't work for everyone. He also finds hope in the healing capacity of the human body.

"Stroke is a brain attack," he explained. "The resulting limitation is due to brain damage. The brain is an amazing organ that is built for our recovery in life events. Neuroplasticity is a term used to describe the brain's ability to learn, change, and improve. We use it every day in everything we do." He pointed out that that capacity to learn and improve does not go away with stroke. "It's always with us. It can do fantastic and phenomenal things. Or it can keep us where we are or decrease our functionality. It depends on how we use it."

One of Steve's stroke-related issues was trouble with short-term memory.

In the past Steve had studied some of memory expert Harry Lorraine's method, and after the stroke, he started studying it again. "*Ageless Memory* is Harry's book. He gives basic techniques, one is a "chain system" of memory, another is called a "peg system," where you memorize according to a number. It gives a context. "Memory palace" is another."

Steve said he's able to remember at least 100 items in and out of order. "I know the 25 amendments to the Constitution, the 50 states and their capitals alphabetically, the 66 books of the Bible, and usually where I can find my car keys!"

When people ask Steve why he wants to remember all those things, he tells them that isn't the point. "The point is it exercises your brain. Your brain's memory acts like a muscle. The more you use it, the more it remembers."

***

These days Steve continues to enjoy life with Melanie—they walk together over three miles, three times per week—and he is enthusiastic about helping other stroke survivors. In the spring of 2021, he joined the board of directors of Stroke Awareness Oregon (SAO).

"It's easy to get real focused on yourself, so I am excited to be on a board because I get to focus on other people again, and not me. That is a good thing."

He wants to help SAO help people find their own motivation to do the work of rehab. "You can tell people anything you want, and it'll be entertaining, but it won't help them unless they find what they care about. That's what I want us to be able to do, help them find that."

Beyond that, he wants SAO to help people set goals, figure out concrete steps to reach them, log their progress, and then monitor that progress. "This is how we can be more effective at helping people recover from their symptoms of stroke and gain back more of what they lost."

"After all, that's what we all want. We all want to gain back what we've lost. It's part of the grieving process, of course, that we all go through, but you still want to gain back as much as you can even if you're resigned to the fact you won't be what you were before. You do have a chance to regain some of it back. I would sign up for that in a minute and my bet is that others would, too."

"I know everyone has a different stroke experience, many of them worse than mine," he reflected. "I've been fortunate. I've had great support. I've had a lot of things go my way, and not everyone has had that."

He is not only interested in helping others get back more of what they've lost. "I've joked that all my weaknesses are much, much worse now. I think my wife would agree with that! But the truth is there are other things I wasn't very good at before that I can get better at now."

"If we can help others," he said, "we help ourselves. Helping others takes the focus off us and makes us care for others which can improve our own motivation to improve. We all need help from others to improve."

He reminds those who feel discouraged because they feel they've "failed" somehow in rehab, that "failure" can be used to modify one's approach, and find a new way to succeed. "You have to keep your hope and never give up."

ROLLING BOLDLY
Geoff Babb

by Kerry Chaput

"I discovered how much I wanted to make a difference."

Geoff Babb will tell you that he didn't suffer a stroke. He will tell you he survived one.

In 2005 Geoff was active in his career as a Bureau of Land Management fire ecologist, and an avid outdoorsman. He scaled rocks and hiked mountain peaks. His world revolved around connecting with nature and people, whether it be fighting wildfires or adventuring with his family through the Pacific Northwest's stunning landscapes. He was an active father of twin boys, Cory and Emory, and a devoted husband to his wife, Yvonne.

On November 10, 2005, he had a headache and vomiting that lasted hours. Thinking it was simply dehydration, he monitored his symptoms and didn't think too much of it. But twelve hours later the headache still persisted, and his speech started slurring. They knew it was time for a trip to the hospital.

"Things started to go downhill," he said. "At one point I couldn't hold my breath for more than a few seconds. They prepared to put me under to give me a breathing tube. I was getting pretty scared by then." He was nervous about leaving his family, or not being what they needed. By 10 p.m. he couldn't move his left side, and by noon the next day, he was on a respirator.

When Yvonne visited him in the ICU the next day, the only thing he could do was blink his eyes. She kept her support positive, but he was fighting a lung infection, so she had to face the fear that he might not make it. Geoff could move his eyebrows and make minimal motions of his head, and so they began to learn new ways to communicate with each other. He started visualizing climbing Sisters mountain near his home in Central Oregon, dreaming of the progress he hoped to make. Yvonne liked to think of his stroke as "just one more mountain to climb."

Days were measured in centimeters of movement, tubes, surgeries, and needles. They learned right away to rejoice in every ounce of improvement, a twitch of a smile, a raise of an eyebrow. His circle of friends and family held the family up, showering them with support. Less than two weeks into his recovery, his firefighter friends hosted a barbecue in the hospital parking lot. The nurses were able to get him in a chair and wheel him to the window, where 50 people below cheered for him. Yvonne propped up his elbow so he could wave back. People continued to show up for their family in so many ways, and it gave them both the strength to keep fighting."

He was convinced that he needed to get out of the hospital. Even the rehabilitation facility didn't feel right. "I wanted to be home. I felt that my progress would be better there." While at rehab, he opted out of the power wheelchair, choosing instead to stay in a manual wheelchair, against the advice from some health-care professionals. It was more work, and painstaking at times. But Geoff needed to feel the movement in his body. He soon discovered another benefit of the manual chair.

"I found that moving slower, I was able to connect with people in the hospital. Those brief but deep connections with people were meaningful. I wouldn't have had those moments if I used the power chair like the therapists wanted me to."

Geoff returned home, and he and Yvonne faced new challenges. The progress Geoff was hoping for at home didn't come. "A new body required a new response," he said. Yvonne remembered that Geoff was so motivated that he wanted to exercise all the time, and over time that eventually began to wear on her. "I was the morning, afternoon, and night shift," she said. "He once said, 'if you could stretch me more,' and I cut him off and said, 'no, I can't do more.'" She took small steps towards a more balanced life for herself by leaning on her support group, and making time for walks with friends, and occasionally biking to work. She learned how to let family and friends assist Geoff with his two-hour nighttime routine so she could get a night off. Geoff was thankful, and his gratitude and patience helped her move forward.

His family faced another mountain to climb once he came home. "You become aware of all the barriers in the world when you are in a wheelchair," Yvonne said. They were all on a new journey and learned as they went. One day Yvonne had a heart to heart with one of their sons, Cory, who was thirteen at the time. "I wanted to explain to him that things were going to be different. He said to me, 'How? My dad is still my dad.' That gave me strength." Moreover, his sons lifted Geoff when he would fall and jumped at any opportunity to help their dad.

***

As soon as he could, Geoff turned to the place that always restored him. Nature. Even sitting in his yard and taking in the fresh air and the views reset his frame of mind. The breeze, the clear air, and the quiet sounds of nature helped settle his worries and refocus him. He decided that nothing was going to stop him from returning to work and getting connected again with nature.

To his delight, his colleagues at the fire camp, whom he calls his summer family, approached him and asked how they could help get him back out in the field the next fire season. They set to work building a yurt with a ramp and access to a special ADA bathroom. The next season, he was out in the field again, creating plans to fight local wildfires. "These men would work 16-hour days and then help Geoff with his clothes and bathing," Yvonne said. "It brought me to tears."

***

Along the rushing Deschutes River in Central Oregon lies a trail that Geoff has traversed many times. It's a special place where pine trees gather, and black lava rock splits the river. Views of waterfalls and the meandering water create a hiker's paradise. Geoff wasn't about to let a stroke stop him from experiencing that again. He knew he needed a wheelchair that could get him into the outdoors. A dream was born. To create a wheelchair that would take him anywhere he desired.

Geoff enlisted the help of his friend Dale, a helicopter mechanic, to modify his regular wheelchair with more rugged tires, a detachable front wheel, handbrakes, and a harness. He called it the "AdvenChair 1.0." With help from friends and family, he hit the trail in his new wheelchair.

Unable to maneuver AdvenChair 1.0 over a difficult patch of rocks, his hiking partners lowered him to the ground, where he experienced the sensation that he remembered from rock climbing. "We had some great adventures in my original AdvenChair," said Geoff, "all of which prepared us for a trip to the bottom of the Grand Canyon in 2016— more or less." After a broken axle on the Bright Angel Trail less than two miles down into the Grand Canyon, nature showed Geoff once again not what he couldn't do, but what he could work towards. The wheelchairs available were not going to cut it, but Geoff wasn't about to give up. It was back to the drawing board. "Each setback is a gift," Geoff said. It provides another opportunity for improvement.

It was time to get creative. Pulling from the creativity he never realized was inside of him, he began to work on the design of an all-terrain wheelchair. He needed something sturdy that could stand up to the rugged terrain of his favorite hiking trails. He knew that his biggest obstacle was not his stroke, but the equipment available to him. He worked with a CAD designer and Yvonne and Dale to create the next version of the AdvenChair, one that could take him back out to the therapeutic power of nature. He believed that with the right chair, nothing was off limits.

***

On November 10, 2017, it all came to a grinding halt when he experienced another stroke, on the other side of his brainstem. Twelve years to the day of his initial incident, he was back in the hospital, fighting through another stroke. Yvonne remembered the doctors shocking his heart to stabilize his atrial fibrillation. "As they're shocking him with the paddles, I was cheering him from behind the curtain in between sobs."

He had to relearn how to swallow, how to speak, and use his right hand. Severe muscle spasms required a pump implanted in his stomach. His body once again fought infection after infection through months in the hospital. People like to joke with him, telling him to avoid November 10 like it's jinxed. He says it's the opposite. "I say it's a day to celebrate. Celebrate the things I've overcome and the gift of discovering what I'm capable of."

Because of his physical limitations, Geoff had to retire. Leaving a decades long career meant having to redefine his identity. He had to say goodbye to his summer family. Instead of focusing on what he'd lost, he put all his energy into his new dream of improving the AdvenChair.

With his newly regained entrepreneurial spirit, he went back to work on the chair with the CAD designer and Yvonne and Dale. The new chair, the AdvenChair 2.0, was revised and improved, tested and improved again. The team finally created a prototype that passed all the tests. It's an all-terrain wheelchair with an adjustable sit-ski seat, adjustable handlebars, 27.5-inch mountain bike wheels, and fitted with high-grade aluminum mountain bike components throughout, scheduled for roll-out in summer 2021. It will be the first of its kind in the world.

Geoff knew that the AdvenChair 2.0 could take him over rocks and along streams, through the Grand Canyon and camping in the forests. What he began to realize, is that it could give others that gift, too. He connected with people on hospice and families with terminally-ill children, all longing for the gift of family time in nature. When he could, he also joined the boards of Healing Reins Therapeutic Riding Center and Oregon Adaptive Sports, both in Bend. When the second stroke took away his career, it gave him the gift of purpose, one that now belonged to helping others.

It's been 15 years of rolling boldly for Geoff Babb, and he has no plans to slow down. Beyond the Grand Canyon, Geoff and Yvonne plan to climb the Great Wall of China and hike the Camino de Santiago, a 500-mile trek through Spain's 15 regions.

"Retiring was an end, but it was also a beginning. It was a chance to focus on a new adventure. I never imagined myself creating something like this, but I soon discovered how much I wanted to make a difference." Geoff committed to his new purpose, and now he loves connecting with others who want to enjoy nature with their families. He likes to quote J. K. Rowling, who wrote: "Fate shoved you through an unexpected door, and you lit the way for others."

***

What helped Geoff and his family through?

On the day Geoff went to the hospital after his first stroke, a community began to form around him, Yvonne, and the boys. Friends near and far sent messages and gifts and words of encouragement. Over time, they organized themselves into teams, some of which helped at home, and others that helped get Geoff back outside. "Our lives have become so rich because of the people around us," Geoff said. "I realized that not only did we need help, but people needed to help us. People have gifts to offer, and our whole journey has been about accepting those gifts." The community of people supporting Geoff and Yvonne and their sons only grows larger with time.

Geoff's strokes challenged him and his family in ways they never thought possible. But it also brightened their lives in unexpected ways. "It's brought us closer as a family."

Geoff's AdvenChair is taking him on physical journeys to all corners of the world, but it has also taken him on a spiritual journey. Through his stroke recovery he not only discovered a motivation to share his gifts with others, but that our physical bodies are no match for the amazing capability of our minds.

Monza Naff, right, and her partner Sharon

LEARNING TO RELEARN

Monza Naff

by Robin Emerson

"Don't lose heart, don't lose heart."

When Monza Naff tells the story of her stroke in February 2016, she'll let go of the struggle to find a word she can't retrieve and allow another word or phrase to take its place.

She seems at ease with hesitations.

When memory falters, she might ask her partner Sharon for a forgotten word. On occasion, she lets out a sigh, but not very often, and when she looks back on what she lost, and what was found, her voice is warm, relaxed, inviting. She'll tell you it's a miracle.

At the age of sixty-seven, while living in Sunriver, OR, Monza survived a stroke that damaged the part of her brain responsible for language. When she regained consciousness in the hospital, she couldn't remember her name. She didn't know the word for nose or ear, couldn't identify a color or a towel or a water glass. But she thought she knew where she *was*. "In the library," she said when asked.

Monza had been a wordsmith all her life—a professor of literature, a Shakespearean scholar, and a poet. Now almost everything was nameless. "Words were my life and they were gone," she said. "Losing my words was like losing myself." Monza had severe aphasia—from the Greek root "aphatos" meaning "speechless." She would have to relearn the entire vocabulary of everyday life.

***

After two weeks in the hospital Monza returned home and met with Brittney, a speech therapist she would work with for the next two years. Neuropsychological testing began. How many animals could she name in 60 seconds (just three—cat, dog, and aardvark), or how many picture cards could she pick out as fruits? Improvement was tracked and Brittney would help Monza see her progress as they went along.

At home, Sharon and Monza started with naming colors—one at a time before they moved on to the next. Point and name, show and name. If Monza could connect the color "blue" with different objects throughout the day, the word became established. She wasn't trying to recall a word that had slipped her mind. It was more like learning a word for the first time, the way a child acquires language through constant exposure.

With a set of flashcards showing household items, they drilled for eight months until Monza had mastered all fifty. Most confounding were compound words like "screwdriver" and "flashlight." The day she looked at a picture of a glass of ice water, and could name all three—water, glass, and ice—was a day of victory. "Even the things that helped, though, were so hard, I sometimes wasn't very nice or grateful about it," Monza said as she looked back.

"Shame damages the connection with the people around us," Sharon said, as she reflected on the emotional roller coaster of recovery. "We live in a world where most people feel inadequate if they have to be helped a lot or they've lost independence in any way. Sometimes, people who have had a stroke get angry at their caretakers because they feel diminished, but there's so much to be found in the love of the people around you. At the end of every day, I would tell Monza, 'OK, here's what you did today. And here's another thing and another thing.' She couldn't remember. To have me emphasize what she'd accomplished—for her to feel that appreciation—was important."

***

One of the obstacles to fluency was a habit that developed in everyday conversation. Monza would stall as she searched for the right word: "Where is the . . . ahh . . . where is the. . . ahh. . . ahhhhh. . ." Sharon created a one-page list of strategies called the "Word Clue List." Embarrassed and angry, Monza refused to use it. She didn't want to use a crib sheet to talk. Sharon told her she had a choice: she could feel ashamed or she could appreciate that people were willing to help. Sharon laminated the sheet so it could be consulted easily, and Monza agreed to try it.

A glance would cue a workaround, some alternative way of conveying what she meant. Friends helped her practice. "Just allow it," they would say if she struggled. The Word Clue List offered myriad ways to get unstuck. "Kitchen" could become "the room where we cook," or a friend with a forgotten name could be "the woman with the horse." She discovered that just by looking at the Word Clue List she had a chance to pause and calm herself. "Stress [was] my enemy," she later said in a speech to an audience of health-care professionals and other stroke survivors.

One day Sharon heard Monza call out in distress, "Come here, c-c-come here." Alarmed, she rushed into the bedroom to find Monza panic-stricken, "What ... what's ... your name? I don't know your name." Monza cried for a long time while Sharon held her. At times, when the brain is working so hard, exhaustion takes over, exhaustion that may not even be recognized as such, exhaustion disguised as despair. Sometimes what is needed is rest.

***

As recovery continued, Monza learned that—instead of fixating on a word she couldn't retrieve as frustration mounted—she could write, spell, draw, or use gestures to convey a meaning.

As Sharon put it: "Anything that kept the mind moving was good, anything that shifted the capacity to communicate to other, undamaged parts of her brain."

Aphasia involves not only the inability to recall words, but also the intrusion of made-up words, syllables strung together to form words that—on the surface—sound nonsensical. As is common in aphasia, Monza didn't know when the words she was using weren't real words. Looking back on the time when she began to email friends, she spoke of aphasia in its most primitive form: "I didn't realize I was doing it, the aphasia . . . it was *bizarre*. People would ask, 'Are you OK?' And I'd wonder, 'Why are they asking me if I'm OK in an *email?*' I didn't get it. Until Sharon showed me some of them. And then I thought, 'Oh my God.' "

But the messages, while still garbled, grew easy to understand. A heartfelt birthday message to a friend:

"Happy Birthday! Happy-go-lucky even more than banthriprille. Keep a great/have a grateful time, and keep a grateful list with me!"

Later still, sounding even more like herself, Monza responded to a friend on Facebook who had posted a dream-like image of a woman in flight:

"Love that fearless energy! Feels my being flies so free trying so hard to fly to each meaning in the languid meetings of words. My head aches from flying."

Monza explained that what helped most with the aphasia-words was when those around her gently pointed them out. Eventually, she reached the point where if one slipped out, she could laugh.

In the spring of 2017, Sharon and Monza traveled to Ashland, a small city in Southern Oregon that holds the famed Oregon Shakespeare Festival each year. This was an opportunity to exercise memory in a special way since at the festival Monza could reconnect with her beloved Shakespeare. They studied the Cliff Notes to prepare and after each play Monza would describe what she'd seen. She had first been exposed to Shakespeare in the eighth grade and, as she watched the performances—*Henry IV, Julius Caesar,* and *The Merry Wives of Windsor,* among them—long-term memory began to restore what she thought had been permanently lost. "I'd go see one, and I'd go, 'Ohhhh, I kinda remember.' It started coming back to me on its own." Flashcards were a thing of the past.

Monza reached the point when she wanted to start writing again. From the beginning, she had mourned the loss of her ability to write her poetry. More than anything, she wanted to reclaim it. One day, when she and Sharon were watching a documentary about Yosemite,

Monza was captivated by a scene of swans beginning their migration. Sharon got the idea of pausing the video at intervals to record Monza's associations. "Just say 'em as we watch 'em," Sharon told her. There was the white of feathers, and of snow, and the black beneath the wings paired with something else, and so on. Monza gathered up what she had always called her "jottings," but couldn't turn them into a poem with structure and rhythm.

After Monza told Brittney about the impasse, Brittney proposed an exercise. Monza was to choose a poem she loved, underline the nouns, put all the verbs in brackets, and substitute her own. "It will be your poem in that form," Brittney told her. "Starlings in Winter" by Mary Oliver became the template, and the stroke surviver who had once called a radio a "rister," and a teapot a "tweezer," who had asked for a "dead carrion" when she wanted a candy bar, and written an email that was nothing but numbers and symbols was on her way toward the first poem she would write since the stroke.

***

In October 2020, Monza suffered a second stroke that left her speech intact, but impaired her balance and coordination, made it difficult for her to swallow, and weakened her right arm, hand, and leg. Even so, when she wheeled herself into the stroke unit's dining room for the first time, she brought along all she had gained back during her first recovery, including her trademark sense of humor.

She described how difficult it was to swallow after the second stroke. "My tongue was stuck over on the side so my food would get stuck behind my tongue . . . I had to get my food out of there and get water so I wouldn't spew food all over the table."

Not only was it difficult to swallow, it was also difficult to get food into her mouth. "We had those rubber utensil grips [to help]," she said, "but it was hard anyway. The peas and carrots—why they always gave us peas and carrots, I don't know—they would always fly. I was mortified. I said to the woman who cleaned up after us, 'If I could hold a broom, I would love to sweep up my peas and carrots.' She said, 'It's *all right,* Monza. Stand up from your wheelchair and look at where everyone else is sitting.' I looked, and peas and carrots, peas and carrots, peas and carrots. I saw it, and I smiled, and went, 'OK. I'll remember that.' I knew by the end of that first meal, 'Ahh, this is the room where the people who have had strokes eat. We're in here together to see what all the other people do, how they eat and how they cough and how they spew.'"

Monza recalled another kindness from the time of the second stroke. "You wear these dumb pants," she said, "and when you have to change them, you can't wipe yourself in your normal way. I just sat there and cried. When I tried to do it with the other hand, I couldn't reach. A nursing assistant came in and said, 'Why are you crying?' and I said, 'I can't wipe myself,' and she said, 'That's what *we're* here for. Let me do it.' After she wiped and washed and dried me, she asked, 'Does that feel better?' And I said, 'Oh, just lots.' She told me, 'Don't forget to ask for help.' That was one of those moments that was the least pleasurable, but it made me feel joy."

***

Having survived not one, but two strokes, Monza believes that whatever the limitations a stroke imposes, you can still see the things, hear the things, say the things, enjoy the things, that mean the most to you. You can grow beyond those limitations in unexpected ways. What you learn becomes a bridge to others. "Don't lose heart, don't lose heart," she says.

AFTERWORD

Do you have a story to tell about stroke?

Maybe you are a partner to a stroke warrior, or a son, daughter, parent, or other relative. Perhaps you are a caregiver, health-care professional, or a stroke warrior yourself. Whoever you are, and whatever your relationship is to stroke, we want to hear your story.

We want to hear your story because this collection of inspiring tales about and for stroke warriors is just the first of a series! We at Stroke Awareness Oregon plan future volumes of *Just Say "Yes" to Life!* to keep raising awareness about stroke, and to keep inspiring warriors and their families with narratives of connection and hope, triumph and resilience, and love and transformation.

To fill those future volumes, though, we need more stories. Your story.

Please send a brief summary of your narrative to:

Stroke Awareness Oregon
695 SW Mill View Way
Bend, OR 97702
Attn: Just Say "Yes" to Life!
or call (541) 323-5641
admin@strokeawarenessoregon.org

We look forward to hearing from you!

STROKE AWARENESS OREGON

In four short years, Stroke Awareness Oregon has made tremendous progress towards our strategic goals, which are 1) to educate about stroke causes and prevention; 2) to make F.A.S.T. a household word; 3) to support the recovery of stroke survivors and their families in their best possible life, and; 4) to do all this life-saving work in collaboration with others.

We have found no other nonprofit in Oregon doing the important work we do to eliminate disability and death from stroke and to support stroke recovery. This book, *Just Say Yes to Life!*, is a project founded in passion and love. It complements other work we've accomplished such as the distribution of thousands of F.A.S.T. postcards, education of hundreds of individuals through our "Stroke 101" presentations, management of four stroke support groups (even during COVID), and partnerships with a variety of providers. Recent data from our local hospital, St. Charles, indicates that since Stroke Awareness Oregon began making F.A.S.T. a household word, they have seen a 30 percent increase in people arriving for stroke treatment in time to receive life-saving treatment and to mitigate the devastating effects of stroke.

And we're not stopping there. Because of the dedication of our board of directors, staff, and volunteers, we plan to expand throughout Central Oregon where rural residents face challenges obtaining stroke diagnosis, transport, and treatment. Our board and staff are drawing up plans for a membership drive to increase stroke awareness, and soon we'll be positioned to offer additional assistance to stroke survivors and their families through a new peer support program.

Frequently, we receive requests from people in other states wishing to learn about Stroke Awareness Oregon, or even to join a Zoom support group. We welcome and strive to assist anyone who asks us for help.

We at Stroke Awareness Oregon invite you to learn more about our life-saving work, contact us for additional information, and support us however you are able.

Won't you join us in making a difference?
www.strokeawarenessoregon.org

What is Stroke Awareness Oregon?

Located in The Old Mill District at 695 Mill View Way, Bend, OR 97702

Time is Brain ...
- For every minute without oxygen, 2 million brain cells die.
- Stroke is the leading cause of disability in the world.
- 80% of strokes are preventable with lifestyle and medical intervention.
- Rapid medical intervention makes a difference in long-term recovery.

That's Why ...
Stroke Awareness Oregon, a nonprofit, is dedicated to awareness of signs & symptoms through education with:
- F.A.S.T.
- Community presentations
- TV commercials
- Distributed print materials

Stroke Awareness Oregon was founded by physicians, stroke survivors & community members.

Stroke Awareness Oregon is dedicated to supporting stroke survivors & their families in recovery & living their best possible life with hope.

We do this through ...
- Support Groups - The Mens Club, Stroke Support, Caregiver Support & Young People's Support Groups. All great online resources and personal support geared to all who are affected by stroke.
- Monthly Educational Lectures - Please subscribe to our newsletter for monthly updates and details.
- Stroke 101 - A ten minute virtual presentation on how to save a life by understanding the warning signs of stroke. Narrated by our board president, Dennis Schaberg, M.D.. Available for churches, service clubs & employers who want to bring awareness to the early signs of stroke and save lives.
- Online Resource Directory
- Social activities & much more!

Stroke Awareness Oregon is dedicated to building partnerships & community relationships to support this life saving work.
- First Responders
- Hospitals
- Medical Providers
- Rehabilitation Professionals
- Community and Business Donors

Here's How You Can Help!
- Become a financial sponsor • Become a monthly donor
- Make a one time donation • Volunteer your time
- Sign-up to our newsletter • Schedule a Stroke 101 presentation for your group or work place
- Distribute F.A.S.T. postcards (English, Spanish or virtual) in your community

695 Mill View Way, Bend, OR 97702 • strokeawarenessoregon.org • 541-323-5641 • 501C3 Tax ID #82-4216575

ACKNOWLEDGEMENTS

Our heartfelt gratitude goes to the nine volunteer writers who contributed their time and expertise to interviewing our stroke warriors and writing such uplifting stories about them.

~ Thank you ~

Lili Alpaugh
Diane Huie Balay
Kerry Chaput
Dana Clark-Millar
Amy J Doherty
Robin Emerson
Glenda "GG" Goodrich
Tom Olsen
Jake Sheaffer

We appreciate the board of directors and staff of Stroke Awareness Oregon for their assistance with this project, Dr. Steven Goins for being a champion since the beginning of our work together, Ellen Santasiero for editorial leadership, Lieve Maas at Bright Light Graphics for book design and production, Jet Cowan at The Hidden Touch for communications and marketing strategy, and Ben Ritt for book project management.

ABOUT THE EDITOR
Ellen Santasiero

Ellen Santasiero believes there is nothing more important than heart-centered human connection.

As an editor and writer, she strives to facilitate this kind of connection through well-edited and well-written stories.

Ellen writes and edits content for a variety of clients and she provides editing and manuscript reviews to individual writers working on fiction and nonfiction manuscripts, plays, and academic papers. Her writing has appeared in literary and other magazines since 2001.

In addition to editing and writing, Ellen teaches at The Forge, a ten-month online creative writing program. She also teaches private memoir classes. From 2007 to 2021, she taught literature and writing at Oregon State University-Cascades in Bend. A native New Yorker, she's made her home in Central Oregon since 1989. She is a co-editor of *Placed: An Encyclopedia of Central Oregon, Vol. 1.*

Contact:

Ellen Santasiero

esantasiero@gmail.com

541-408-4509

Web site: ellensantasiero.com

Writing samples: esantasiero.journoportfolio.com

The Forge: theforgewriting.com

WRITER BIOGRAPHIES

Lili Alpaugh, a native of New Orleans, has made Bend, OR her home for more than a decade. She loves the outdoors, writing memoir and essays, studying history, and travel. She is a retired physical therapist and has a passion for helping people with disabilities.

Diane Huie Balay is a retired journalist and book author who was widely published nationally and internationally while she was an associate editor at the Dallas-based *United Methodist Report*. Now living in the California Central Coast wine country, she delights in spending time with her eight grandchildren.

Born in California wine country, **Kerry Chaput** began writing shortly after earning her Doctorate in Physical Therapy. Her love of storytelling began with a food blog and now she writes historical novels. She lives in Bend, OR with her husband, two daughters, and two rescue pups. www.kerrywrites.com or Twitter @ChaputKerry.

Dana Clark-Millar has published articles about professional endurance athletes, including a series she created about the women of the endurance world. Her current writing interests have taken her on a deep dive into the world of haiku. When she is not counting syllables on her fingers, she is using them to dig in the dirt in her garden.

Amy J Doherty is a writer, marketing professional, yoga teacher, wife, and mother to two sons and a rescue dog named Nacho. She is currently working on a collection of stories about her son's epilepsy and appreciates her fellow writers committed to the Morning Zoom Crew.

Robin Emerson is a retired clinical social worker. Her interest in writing about stroke recovery followed a fall that resulted in a traumatic brain injury. She is a student of aikido working toward her black belt with the Oregon Ki Society. She lives with her husband in Bend, OR. remerson1265@gmail.com

Glenda "GG" Goodrich is a writer, mixed media artist, art doula, and SoulCollage® facilitator living in Salem, OR. As an artist, friend, mother and grandmother, nature lover and journeyer, she feel closest to her own soul when creating art, teaching her grandchildren to love the earth, and sharing art and SoulCollage® with others.

Tom Olsen has enjoyed writing as an avocation for 50 years. His work has appeared in *The Bulletin, Central Oregon Boomer and Senior News, 48 Degrees North, Northwest Magazine,* and other publications. Tom enjoys sailing, cooking, and gardening with his life partner, Karen, and their spunky Maltese, Garbo.

Ellen Santasiero is the editor of *Just Say "Yes" to Life!,* and a co-editor of *Placed: An Encyclopedia of Central Oregon, Vol. 1.* Her writing has appeared in *Northwest Review, Marlboro Review, The Sun, Oregon Humanities, High Desert Journal,* and in *Going Green,* an anthology from the University of Oklahoma Press. She lives in Bend, OR. ellensantasiero.com

Jake Sheaffer grew up in the farmland of Southwestern Pennsylvania. He holds a BA in business. A writer of contemporary short stories and science fiction, his work has appeared in art journals in Western Maryland and Central Oregon. Jake enjoys lakes and rivers, rye whiskey with friends, and mountain hikes. jakesheaffer.wixsite.com/timeinbend or Instagram @jg_sheaffer_17

RESOURCES

Organizations

AdvenChair

"All-terrain wheelchair with adjustable sit-ski seat, adjustable handlebars, 27.5-inch mountain bike wheels and high-grade aluminum mountain bike components throughout."
www.advenchair.com

American Stroke Association

The American Stroke Association "teams with millions of volunteers to prevent, treat, and beat stroke by funding innovative research, fighting for stronger public health policies, and providing life-saving tools and information."
www.stroke.org

AMES™

Assisted Movement with Enhanced Sensation technology is *iotech*'s first commercially ready market offering. AMES is a patented, FDA 510(k)-cleared, robotic rehabilitative exercise technology that has been clinically proven in over 400 patients to improve movement and functionality of patients' arms, wrists, hands, fingers, legs, ankles, and toes.
www.iotech.vmg1.com

Aphasia Access

Aphasia Access is "committed to anyone on the front lines of aphasia care as well as to breaking down the communication access barriers that are all too prevalent in our health care delivery systems." *www.aphasiaaccess.org*

Believe - Stroke Recovery Foundation
Believe - Stroke Recovery Foundation provides "stroke and brain injury survivors with financial assistance and resources to help them better control and manage their journey to recovery."
www.believesrf.org

Central Oregon Radiology Associates (CORA)
"CORA and Cascade Medical Imaging offer services at St. Charles Health System throughout Central and Eastern Oregon. CORA also provides imaging services to Harney District Hospital, Blue Mountain Hospital, Wallowa Memorial Hospital, Lake District Hospital, and several other nearby medical providers. CORA offers innovative techniques, treatments, and procedures in conjunction with state-of-the-art equipment and highly trained staff. Today, CORA is both the largest and the leading medical imaging company in Central and Eastern Oregon.
www.centraloregonradiology.com

MOVAIDO - Feldenkrais Movement Institute
Lifelong athlete, martial artist, and coach Dwight Pargee, MS, GCFP, holds degrees in Exercise Physiology, Sport Science, and Biomechanics. In his practice in Bend, OR, he enjoys opening possibilities for the neurologically impaired, and works with a range of clients from those managing complex chronic pain issues and injury recovery to those refining high-level performance and redefining limits. He has a special curiosity in dynamic balance and stability, applied biomechanics, and neuromuscular learning.
www.facebook.com/Movaido

Oregon Adaptive Sports
Oregon Adaptive Sports provides life-changing outdoor experiences for individuals with disabilities, including stroke survivors. OAS specializes in providing access to state-of-the-art adaptive sports equipment and individualized support to create safe and successful year-

round outdoor experiences. OAS programs are offered at low or no cost to participants, and scholarships are available.
www.oregonadaptivesports.org

Oregon Stroke Network

Oregon Stroke Network "is a nonprofit organization comprised of a variety of health-care professionals in many practice settings across the state who care for patients diagnosed with stroke."
www.oregonstrokenetwork.org

Pacific Stroke Association

The Pacific Stroke Association's mission is "to reduce the incidence of stroke through education and to help alleviate stroke's devastating aftermath through programs that support survivors and caregivers.
www.pacificstrokeassociation.org

Power of Patients

Power of Patients is a "free, customizable, and easy-to-use dashboard for tracking brain injury symptoms and triggers. In combination with our educational resources and clinical trial opportunities, Power of Patients engages, informs, and empowers the brain injury community."
www.powerofpatients.com

Santa Clara Valley Medical Center

The Rehabilitation Center at SCVMC is a 64-bed full-service physical rehab facility licensed by the State of California and located in San Jose. Specialties include treating individuals with brain injury, spinal cord injury, stroke, and other disabling neurological conditions. Outpatient Physical Medicine & Rehabilitation clinic and therapies are also available.
www.scvmc.org

St. Charles Health System - Oregon

"With medical centers in Bend, Redmond, Prineville, and Madras hospitals and more than 220 employed medical providers, St. Charles Health System is the largest provider of medical care in Central Oregon. We take our role in our communities seriously and have pledged to work with our partners to achieve our vision: Creating America's healthiest community, together. St. Charles Bend is Oregon's only Level II Trauma Center east of the Cascades. St. Charles Prineville and St. Charles Madras are critical access hospitals that are well regarded in their commitment to modern, progressive health care."
www.stcharleshealthcare.org

Stroke Awareness Oregon

Stroke Awareness Oregon's goals are to "educate the community on how to recognize stroke, make F.A.S.T. a household word, develop resources and support for stroke patients and their families, and increase awareness about stroke prevention."
www.strokeawarenessoregon.org

Strength After Stroke

BASE, a fifteen-module course, helps participants navigate and process the mental and emotional challenges of stroke recovery through Belief, Attitude, Strength, and Energy.
www.strengthafterstroke.com

Stroke Onward

Stroke Onward's mission is "to provide stroke survivors, families and caregivers with more resources to help them navigate the emotional journey to rebuild their identities and rewarding lives."
www.strokeonward.com

Summit Health

"Summit Health is a physician-led, patient-centric network committed to delivering a more intuitive, comprehensive, and responsive

care experience for every stage of life and health condition through high-quality primary, specialty, and urgent care. Summit Health has more than 2,000 providers and over 200 locations in New Jersey and New York, as well as more than 130 providers and six locations in Central Oregon."
www.smgoregon.com

Videos

"A Story of Hope" by Kim O'Kelley-Leigh, *www.youtube.com*
"My Stroke of Luck" by Diane M. Barnes, *www.youtube.com*
Rehab Demonstrations and Support Group recordings by Ralph Preston, *www.youtube.com*
"Seeing the Potential in Brain Recovery" by Mike Studer *www.youtube.com*

Books

Be The Good: Becoming a Force for a Better World by Ken Streater, Aviva, 2020
Emerging From the Smoke: A Collection of Warrior Voices, by Orlena Shek, forthcoming Archway Publishing from Simon & Schuster, 2021
Identity Theft: Rediscovering Ourselves After Stroke by Debra Meyerson, Andrews McMeel Publishing, 2019
Relentless by Ted Baxter, Greenleaf Book Group Press, 2018
Silent M.A.G.I.C. and Other Remedies by Kim O'Kelley-Leigh, *lulu.com*, 2010
Stroke Forward: How to Become Your Own Healthcare Advocate … One Step at a Time by Marcia Moran, Moran Consulting, 2019
The Gift of Courage: Stories of Open Hearts, Kindness, and Community by Ken Streater, Aviva, 2020
The Tales of a Stroke Patient by Joyce Hoffman, Xlibris US, 2012

Blogs and Columns

"In For the Long Haul" by Ralph Preston
"My Story" by Alan Wick
"Stroke Tales" by Joyce Hoffman

Contact our Stroke Warriors

Angie Kirk: pak34@aol.com
Gunner Mench: gunnnr@hawaii.rr.com
Keith Taylor: keith@strengthafterstroke.com
Lawnae Hunter: lhunter@strokeawarenessoregon.org
Kim O'Kelley-Leigh: kimmacc@yahoo.com
Roz Dapar: Instagram @zsazsastroke.50

SAO

STROKE AWARENESS OREGON

LET'S TALK ABOUT STROKE

For exciting new updates on the book, please take a look at our book website by scanning the QR Code Below! *https://www.storiesofstroke.com*

If you, or someone you know, has been touched by stroke please join us at Stroke Community! Here, we have members that stretch across numerous demographics in support of one another's journey, career, and lives! This is a website that unites stroke warriors virtually and creates an inclusive community to connect. Stroke Community is the first online platform that establishes our very own tribe in recognition of our journeys. *https://stroke.community*